CAS Paper 19

The 'greenhouse effect' and UK agriculture

Papers and poster displays presented at a conference organised by the Centre for Agricultural Strategy, sponsored by the Ministry of Agriculture, Fisheries and Food and held at The Royal Society, London SW1 on July 14th 1989.

Edited by R M Bennett

Centre for Agricultural Strategy
University of Reading
1 Earley Gate
Reading RG6 2AT

December 1989

1

ISBN 0 7049 0988 X
ISSN 0141 1330

Printed at the College of Estate Management, Reading

90   05863

Originally established by the Nuffield Foundation in 1975, the Centre for Agricultural Strategy is a self-financing unit within the Faculty of Agriculture and Food at the University of Reading.

STAFF

Director	Professor C R W Spedding, CBE
Deputy Director	Professor J S Marsh
Assistant Director	Dr J C Tayler
Personal Assistant to the Director	Miss A M Hoxey
Senior Research Fellows	Dr S P Carruthers Mr R B Tranter
Research Fellows	Mrs D M Bather Mrs G M Craig Mr C E Flint Mr P J Jones Mrs F A Miller
Research Associate	Mrs T E Wise
Secretaries	Mrs M H Baker Mrs R M J Husain
Honorary Research Fellows	Dr J T Done Dr K A Hassall Mr B J Marshall Dr P J Smith Mr P H Starkey Professor Tilo L V Ulbricht
Consultants (part-time)	Professor A K Giles Professor D R Harvey Dr A J Errington Mr R M Bennett Dr D Hallam Dr T Rehman

Contents

POSTER PRESENTATIONS

Preface

Two of the main functions of the Centre are to identify major issues with long-term implications which require discussion, and to provide a forum for such discussions and debates, whilst helping to ensure that they are well informed.

With increasing concerns surrounding the enhanced 'greenhouse effect' and its implications for climate and environmental change, the Centre thought it timely to organise a conference to widen and inform the debate on the implications for agriculture in the United Kingdom. These published proceedings are a record not only of the excellent papers presented by the speakers at the Conference and of the discussions following them, but also of a number of poster displays exhibited by those involved in past and current research of direct relevance to the topic.

The possible impacts of the 'greenhouse effect' are highly uncertain. This is due not only to the uncertainties of climate change, particularly at a localised level, and the timing of such change, but also due to the added uncertainties surrounding the future economic and policy environment.

Considerable attention is currently being paid to ways of limiting and reducing the release of 'greenhouse gases'. However, evidence suggests that climatic changes due to the enhanced 'greenhouse effect' will still occur during the next century, even if action to reduce 'greenhouse gases' is taken now. Thus knowledge and discussions of the implications for agriculture of the 'greenhouse effect' are of great importance to strategies concerning the future of agricultural production and land use.

C R W Spedding
Director
Centre for Agricultural Strategy

Abbreviations

AAR	Annual Average Rainfall
ADAS	Agricultural Development and Advisory Service
AFRC	Agricultural and Food Research Council
°C	Degrees Centigrade
CAP	Common Agricultural Policy (of the EC)
CAS	Centre for Agricultural Strategy
CFCs	Chlorofluorocarbons
CH_4	Methane
cm	Centimetres
CO_2	Carbon Dioxide
cv	Cultivar
d°C	Day Degrees (Centigrade)
DM	Dry Matter
DOE	Department of the Environment
EC	European Community
EHS	Experimental Horticulture Stations
FRG	Federal Republic of Germany
ft	Feet
g	Grams
G	Giga 10^9 (thousand million)
GATT	General Agreement on Tariffs and Trade
GCMs	General Circulation Models
GDP	Gross Domestic Product
GDR	German Democratic Republic
GE	Gross Energy
GISS	Goddard Institute for Space Studies
ha	Hectares
IIASA	International Institute for Applied Systems Analysis
in	Inches
km	Kilometres
l	Litres
LAI	Leaf Area Index

9

LCT	Lower Critical Temperature
m	Metres
M	Million
MAFF	Ministry of Agriculture, Fisheries and Food
ME	Metabolisable Energy
mg	Milligrams
MJ	Megajoules
mm	Millimetres
MRL	Maximum Residue Level
Mt	Million tonnes
N	Nitrogen
N_2O	Nitrous Oxide
O_2	Oxygen
O_3	Ozone
pH	A measure of acidity or alkalinity
ppbv	Parts per billion by volume
ppmv	Parts per million by volume
SMD	Soil Moisture Deficit
SO_2	Sulphur Dioxide
t	Tonnes
T_A	Temperature an animal experiences
T_C	Climatic temperature
UCT	Upper Critical Temperature
UK	United Kingdom
UN	United Nations
US	United States (of America)
USSR	Union of Soviet Socialist Republics

Glossary

ANAEROBIC — Without oxygen

ANHOLOCYCLIC — Without a sexual phase in the life cycle

ANTHROPOGENIC — Human

BIOSPHERE — The part of the earth and its atmosphere where living things are found

BIOTA — The fauna and flora of a region

CRYOSPHERE — Parts of the earth and its atmosphere which are below freezing

HARVEST INDEX — $= \dfrac{\text{Economic (useful) yield}}{\text{Total biomass}}$

MONOGASTRIC — Single stomach (eg pigs are monogastric animals)

ONTOGENY — The whole of the development of an organism from fertilization to completion of the life history

PATHOGEN — A disease-causing organism

PHENOLOGY — Visible characteristics of a plant or animal (as opposed to genetic)

PHEROMONES — Chemical substances facilitating communication between organisms of the same species (mainly animals)

PHOTOSYNTHESIS — The process in green plants by which carbohydrates are synthesised from water and carbon dioxide using the energy of sunlight

RHIZOSPHERE — The area around plant roots

SEMIOCHEMICALS — Chemical substances which transmit signals

STRATOSPHERE — Layer of atmosphere above the troposphere

TAKE-ALL — A disease of cereals due to the soil-borne fungus *Gaeumannomyces graminis*

TROPOSPHERE — Lower atmosphere

Bennett, R M (Ed) (1989) *The 'greenhouse effect' and UK agriculture*. CAS Paper 19. Reading: Centre for Agricultural Strategy.

Opening Address

by the **Rt Hon John MacGregor MP**,
Minister of Agriculture, Fisheries and Food

I am delighted to open this Conference on the impact of the greenhouse effect on UK agriculture. I am very pleased that my Department has been able to sponsor the event and should like to congratulate Professor Spedding for organising it.

The Conference is well timed. It is a follow-up to the Prime Minister's seminar on global warming. The Conference is also taking place at a time when the international collaborative discussions are getting into top gear.

The Government's view is that the problems associated with global warming must be addressed internationally. We have recently proposed the negotiation of an umbrella convention. Our initiative has received general support, and work on it is now under way internationally.

My Department is very much involved in these discussions. We are a member of the Working Group of the Inter-governmental Panel on Climate Change which is considering, amongst other things, the possible response strategies in the agricultural sector and for coastal defences. I look to your Conference today to inform and assist us in the development of our approach on this complex issue.

At this stage, we can only make a very broad assessment of the possible effects on UK agriculture under various climatic change scenarios. These may or may not prove to be accurate. Current predictions of the rate and magnitude of climatic change are subject to considerable uncertainty. The current consensus opinion is however that, assuming the effective doubling of greenhouse gas concentrations, global warming might average between 1.5 and 4.5°C by the end of the next century. To those who argue today that the problem is already with us, or will be so within a year or two, my response is that, first, the greenhouse effect is a long-term not a sudden phenomenon and, second, climatic evidence is still inconclusive. The general trend in annual average temperatures is consistent with global warming, but still within the natural range of variation over a period of centuries. Recent events such as mild winters in Britain or the US drought are still more likely to be exceptional events within existing patterns, rather than a new pattern already upon us.

We are therefore concerned to assess the likely impact not in the short-term but in the longer-term, not next year but next century.

The difficulty of making this assessment is compounded by the even greater uncertainty about the prediction of regional climate changes. While some broad generalisations can be made, specific regional forecasts are unlikely to be possible for 15 or 20 years.

A considerable amount of research is being carried out internationally to improve the current assessments, and the Government is making a substantial contribution to this effort. We are spending £15 M this financial year on research which is directly relevant to understanding climate change, including a £1 M programme relevant to the defence of our coastline against sea-level rise. This work is not being carried out in isolation. Much of it will complement work being carried out in other countries.

That brings me directly to the question of coastal defences, which is of course significant for agriculture – the topic of this Conference – as well as for many other aspects of our national life.

Last year my Department spent about £28 M on coastal defence works. I attached particular priority to increasing our expenditure on flood defences in our 3 year Public Expenditure plans for the Ministry, and as a result it has already been agreed that by the year 1991/92 the capital programme of water authority grant-aided work will increase by about 40% compared to that in 1988/89.

During the next century this amount seems certain to increase considerably. For example, up to now, flood defence works have been constructed to allow for a rise in sea level of 30 cm per 100 years. This is double the rate of rise which is estimated to have taken place globally over the early part of this century and therefore at first sight might appear to have some margin of safety. But rises over the next decades could well exceed this rate. Since many defence works can be effective for 50 years or more, this subject is very much in the forefront of our minds at present.

To give us more information, we have already installed a network of tide gauges which actually measure sea levels. Measurements from these tide gauges enable rises in mean sea level to be monitored. This information is not, of course, predictive but it does help to guide other investigation currently underway on the longer-term effects. As our predictions of the degree and rate of future sea level improve – and the way changing weather patterns will interact with this – we will be better placed to respond in the most effective manner.

Turning to the more direct consequences of the greenhouse effect for agriculture, there are several questions which must be addressed, obviously mainly for the longer-term. Agriculture Councils in the Community have a tendency to address only issues requiring urgent or very early resolution, but I am all for considering these longer-term issues now, not least to ensure that anything we do in the Common Agricultural Policy or in domestic agricultural and environmental policies now is compatible with the longer-term scenarios. For example, one of the advantages of set-aside as one part of the policy for dealing with arable surpluses, is that should the worldwide supply and demand situation change for any reason, and there is in consequence a need for us rapidly to increase production, say of cereals in the UK, that adjustment can easily and quickly be made.

I hope this Conference can make a valuable contribution to tackling at least some of these questions.

First, there is the impact of the greenhouse effect on the type of crops and livestock that can be grown and reared in the UK. For example will we be able to grow grain maize or sunflowers in the southern part of the UK? What will happen to rainfall patterns, since this will have a critical effect on livestock production? Could we envisage New Zealand grazing conditions in the UK?

Second, what will happen to yields? Will yield increases be the norm as a result of higher CO_2 concentrations and a warmer climate, or could lower rainfall or other causes actually lead to yield reductions?

Third, what are the possible implications for pest and disease control? A warmer climate, especially in the winter, could lead to more rapid build up of pest populations. Would this make it difficult, for example, to maintain the existing plant health advantages of potato growing in Scotland or will other research developments in the intervening period make this less of a potential problem anyway?

Fourth, the greenhouse effect will also radically affect production patterns throughout the rest of the World. What impact will this have on feeding the needy? What are the implications for world prices and trade and for international trade policies generally? In particular, what will be the implications for agricultural production and policy in the EC?

Last but not least there is the impact on the appearance and environment of our countryside. A warmer climate would offer greater potential for agricultural production in the north and up the hillside. But this could put at risk the important semi-natural habitat found there. What measures will be needed to safeguard this natural heritage? Could we encounter an entirely new range of problems such as erosion and forest fires, which are now commonplace in the Mediterranean area?

None of these questions have easy or clear-cut answers. Not least, much more information is required on the likely extent and pace of climatic change. Many changes will be slow and imperceptible.

But waiting for things to happen will not do. The Government is committed to tackling the problems of research and policy analysis now. This Conference is a valuable part of this process. I wish you well and look forward to studying your conclusions.

Bennett, R M (Ed) (1989) *The 'greenhouse effect' and UK agriculture*. CAS Paper 19. Reading: Centre for Agricultural Strategy.

1 The 'greenhouse effect'

John Bowman

INTRODUCTION

The phrase 'the greenhouse effect' refers to a naturally occurring phenomenon with respect to the earth's radiative balance. The earth-atmosphere system is heated by a net absorption of short-wave radiation from the sun. In an equilibrium state, this is balanced (over a specified period) by a net emission of long-wave (infra-red) radiation from the earth-atmosphere system to space. Certain atmospheric gases are relatively transparent to the incoming short-wave radiation, but they are efficient absorbers of the out-going long-wave radiation and re-radiate it both to space and back to the surface. In this way, such gases effectively 'trap', near the surface, long-wave radiation that would otherwise escape from the earth. They are termed 'greenhouse gases' and the radiative mechanism which influences the temperature of the atmosphere, the 'greenhouse effect'. The basic physical mechanism is well established and understood.

A simplified description of the earth radiation balance is shown in Figure 1. The incoming solar (short-wave) radiation is shown as 100 notional units and the other units in Figure 1 are related to that level. Thus of the 100 units of incoming radiation:

(i)   19 units are absorbed by water vapour, dust, and ozone in the atmosphere;

(ii)   4 units are absorbed by clouds;

(iii) 46 units are absorbed by the earth (on land and at sea);

(iv) 8 units are reflected back into space by the earth's atmosphere;

(v)   17 units are reflected back into space by clouds;

(vi) 6 units are reflected back into space by the earth's surface.

Figure 1
Simplified diagram of the earth's radiation balance

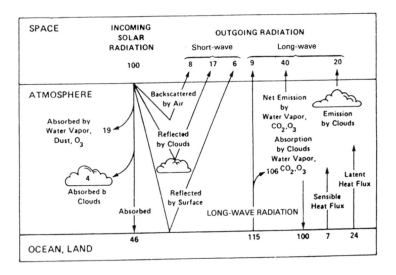

For the earth's system to stay in equilibrium, and for there to be no change in the earth's or the atmospheric temperature, the incoming radiation has to be balanced by an equivalent level, 100 units, of outgoing radiation. 31 units have already been accounted for by reflection of incoming radiation back into space – items (iv), (v) and (vi) – leaving a further 69 units to be accounted for by emission of long-wave radiation to space. These additional outgoing units of long-wave radiation are represented by:

- (vii) 115 units emitted from the earth (on land and at sea); of which 9 units are emitted to space, 100 units are reabsorbed by the earth and 6 units are absorbed by clouds, water vapour, carbon dioxide and ozone;
- (viii) 40 units emitted to space by water vapour, carbon dioxide and ozone;
- (ix) 20 units emitted to space by clouds.

The 60 units (items (viii) and (ix)) of outgoing long-wave radiation lost from the atmosphere are balanced by incoming radiation – items (i) (19 units) and (ii) (4 units) above, 6 units from item (vii) – together with a sensible heat flux of 7 units and a latent heat flux of 24 units from the earth to the atmosphere.

Thus the balance is maintained by 100 units of incoming radiation being offset by 100 units of outgoing radiation (items (iv), (v), (vi), (vii) (9 units), (viii) and (ix) above).

The principal naturally occurring greenhouse gas is water vapour, but other gases, most significantly carbon dioxide (CO_2) as well as methane (CH_4), ozone (O_3), nitrous oxide (N_2O) and chlorofluorocarbons, such as CFC11 and CFC12, also contribute to the effect. In the absence of the greenhouse effect, the temperature at the earth's surface would be some 30°C lower than it is now. The greenhouse effect is vital, therefore, for sustaining life as we know it on the earth. Changes in the level of greenhouse gases in the atmosphere are likely to affect the radiation balance and in ways which we are not able to predict with any degree of certainty.

EARTH HISTORY AND THE GREENHOUSE EFFECT

As a result of research on sediments containing plankton remains, it has been possible to develop a historical record of the earth's atmospheric temperature extending over the last 850 000 years. This record indicates average temperature changes of about 9°C at different periods, with more marked changes in temperature possible in certain regions of the World. The World has experienced a sequence of cold-glacial and warm-interglacial periods, which appear to be linked to cyclic effects with intervals of a little more than 21 000, 41 000 and 100 000 years. These cycles are related respectively to the precession of the earth's axis of rotation, to changes in the angle at which the earth is tilted toward the sun and to changes in the shape of the earth's orbit around the sun.

Research on the chemistry of the sediments has also revealed that there have been variations in the carbon dioxide content of the earth's atmosphere which are in accord with variations in the temperature. When carbon dioxide levels are high the temperature is high, as shown in Figure 2. Particularly significant, is the finding that variations in the relationship of the earth to the sun occur before increases in carbon dioxide in the atmosphere. It is considered that changes in the radiative balance of the earth lead to temperature change but that the relationship is modified by changes in biological productivity, particularly in high latitude seas. Thus a high temperature and a high carbon dioxide content in the atmosphere lead to high biological productivity, which then reduces the carbon dioxide in the atmosphere by major deposition of marine organisms, many with calcium based skeletons – the chalk marine deposits. Reduced carbon dioxide in the atmosphere then leads to reduced earth temperature.

But for the arrival of man in large numbers on earth, these cycles of temperature and carbon dioxide change would have continued. Indeed, the prediction is that but for the effects of man, the earth should just be entering its next glacial period.

CHANGES IN GREENHOUSE GAS LEVELS RESULTING FROM MAN'S ACTIVITIES

What now gives acute cause for concern, is the evidence of significant, recent increases in concentrations of several atmospheric, radiatively active, greenhouse gases. The resulting enhanced greenhouse effect may disturb the current radiative balance and is predicted to bring about significant climate changes by the middle of the next century. The most significant atmospheric change until recently, has been the steady rise in the concentration of atmospheric carbon dioxide since the start of the Industrial Revolution. At 350 ppmv it is now about 30% higher than at the start of industrialisation and is rising at approximately 0.4% (1.5 ppmv) per year. This rise is attributed mainly to the burning of fossil fuels (coal, oil and gas). Deforestation is also believed to be a significant contributory factor.

Scientists have been concerned since the end of the 19th Century about a build up of carbon dioxide in the atmosphere. Much more recent is the realisation that other less-abundant atmospheric trace gases are also increasing, due mainly to man's activities. These other radiatively active trace gases include, in particular, methane (CH_4), nitrous oxide (N_2O), tropospheric (lower-atmosphere) ozone (O_3) and some chlorofluorocarbons (CFCs). A great deal more research is needed to identify and quantify the various sources, sinks and effects of these gases. However, it is known that:

(i) atmospheric concentration of methane is increasing at 1.1% (18 ppbv) per year from its current level of approximately 1.7 ppmv. It is a very effective greenhouse gas. The increase during the last 300 years corresponds well with the growth in world population and the primary source is conversion of organic material by microbes in anaerobic conditions. Variations between estimates of individual sources (rice paddies, swamps, wetlands, natural gas, etc) are extremely large and present the largest uncertainty;

(ii) atmospheric concentration of nitrous oxide is increasing from a baseline of 0.310 ppmv by approximately 0.3% per year (1 ppbv). The sources identified, which include agricultural emissions, biomass and fossil fuel burning, and nitrification in ocean water, are diverse and poorly quantified. However, the upward trend appears to result from fuel combustion and applied fertilizers;

Figure 2

Long-term records from ice cores show the relationship between changes in atmospheric temperature and carbon dioxide content

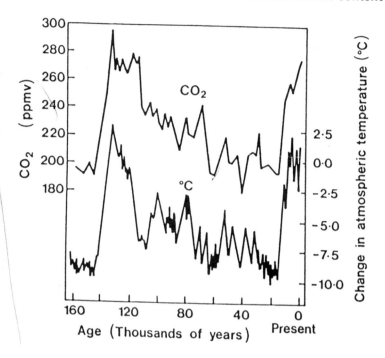

(iii) tropospheric ozone concentrations are variable and are in the range 10-100 ppbv (high in urban areas) and the average concentration is estimated to have doubled since pre-industrial times. A major fraction of this is believed to result from sunlight acting on hydrocarbons and nitrogen oxides in the atmosphere (ie it is an indirect product of fuel combustion);

(iv) CFCs are used as aerosol propellants, refrigerants and cleaning solvents. They are long-lived and are very effective greenhouse gases, some 10 000 times more radiatively active, molecule for molecule, than carbon dioxide. CFCs have shown a steady increase in atmospheric concentration at about 6% per annum and CFC-11 ($CFCl_3$) and CFC-12 (CF_2Cl_2) are estimated to account for about 18% of any global warming, assuming the Montreal Protocol to be effective in limiting CFC production.

Table 1
Comparison of the radiative 'effectiveness' of the greenhouse gases

Gas	Present concentration and increase (ppmv)		Radiative index[1]
Carbon Dioxide (CO_2)	350	+0.4% pa	1
Methane (CH_4)	1.7	+1.1% pa	30
CFCs (CFC – 11 and 12)	0.0006	+6% pa[2]	10000
Nitrous Oxide (N_2O)	0.3	+0.3% pa	150
Tropospheric Ozone (O_3)	0.001–0.1	+0.25% pa[3]	2000

1 Radiative index is the relative contribution to greenhouse warming per molecule.
2 Assumes production governed by Montreal Protocol.
3 Uncertainty of estimates of increase.

Source: Reproduced from Boyle & Ardill (1989).

The effects of these gases on the radiative transparency of the earth's atmosphere are very different, as shown in Table 1. Per molecule, carbon dioxide has the least effect, whilst methane, nitrous oxide, ozone and CFCs have greater effects on radiative transparency. Thus a very small change in the atmospheric content of CFCs may have at least a comparable effect on the earth's radiative balance to a large increase in the carbon dioxide content. The estimated contributions to the earth's temperature change resulting from the changes in atmospheric composition due to man's activities are shown in Table 1. Clearly, a reduction in the emissions of carbon dioxide is little more important than reduction in the emission of methane, nitrous oxide and CFCs. There is an added perceived complication to the story, in that CFCs are considered to be the cause of stratospheric ozone depletion, leading to increased ultra-violet radiation reaching the earth's surface from space. Ultra-violet radiation is damaging to genetic and photosynthetic material, and increased levels at the earth's surface may inhibit the biological productivity of the oceans, especially in high latitudes where ozone depletion is most severe. Reduced marine biological productivity might lead to further changes to the earth's temperature balance. This is still very speculative and much research needs to be done urgently to improve our understanding of natural processes and our predictive capability.

EVIDENCE OF AN ENHANCED GREENHOUSE EFFECT
Global climate is governed by complex and incompletely understood natural

physical processes in, and between, the various interactive components of the climate system (ie atmosphere, oceans, land, biosphere and cryosphere). There have been significant long-term natural changes in climate (especially the glacial and interglacial periods), as well as marked short-term variability. Natural short-term variability and local extreme weather episodes do not, of themselves, indicate a climate change. The increases in greenhouse gas concentrations from 1860 to the present are thought large enough to produce a long-term equilibrium global mean warming of about 1–2°C. However, the actual change in temperature to date is not so easy to estimate. Any warming is likely to be delayed by the large thermal inertia of the oceans, and simplified ocean-atmosphere models suggest that the warming to date should be in the range of 0.5 – 1.0°C. Analyses of observational records show that the global mean surface temperature has warmed by about 0.5°C since 1900. In particular, the six warmest years have occurred in the 1980s – 1988 being the warmest on record. However, there is less agreement amongst climatologists about the global temperatures in the period 1850–1900, during which some believe temperatures may have reached values up to 0.3° warmer than in the early part of this century. Nevertheless, both northern and southern hemispheres appear to have experienced an increase in mean surface temperature over the past 130 years. Although it is not certain that this is the result of increasing concentrations of greenhouse gases, its overall direction and magnitude lie within the estimated range of their effects. Nevertheless, we still do not have direct evidence for cause and effect.

The apparent agreement between the overall observed and predicted rises in global temperature since 1900 may be fortuitous. There is considerable variability during the period that cannot be ascribed to greenhouse gases alone. For example, from the 1950s to the 1970s the global mean temperature changed very little and the northern hemisphere actually cooled. Analyses of climatic records and models of the climate system show that natural climatic variability is very complex. Any temperature increase to date resulting from an enhanced greenhouse effect is still small enough to be masked by natural climate variations. The observed warming then is not yet large enough to establish 'beyond reasonable doubt' that it is due to an enhanced greenhouse effect, and we may have to wait for several decades before we can do so.

The issue of whether anomalous weather events, such as the recent US drought and the mild, dry winter in north-west Europe, are related to an overall warming trend has not yet been resolved. The cause of such weather variability may be linked to cooling of the Equatorial Pacific. However, this emphasises the complexity of the World's weather and climate systems and the role of oceans in these systems. Increased understanding of these processes will also lead to the development of more accurate predictive models of climate change.

In spite of a lack of scientifically incontrovertible evidence, many scientists now believe that the 'observed' global warming this century is, at least in part, a direct consequence of the continuous build up of the concentrations of greenhouse gases, due to anthropogenic activities and the consequent enhanced greenhouse effect. Climatic variability, particularly at decadal and longer timescales, is not well understood and the available records of the very recent past cannot be explained simply in terms of the observed increases in atmospheric concentrations of greenhouse gases. Nevertheless, many scientists now believe that the most plausible explanation for the general global warming trend this century is an enhanced greenhouse effect.

It is important to stress that the current inability to detect, beyond all doubt, a climatic response to the measured increase in greenhouse gases is not central to the issue. Current understanding, predictions and concern are based on our appreciation of the physical basis of the greenhouse effect and its influence on climate and on a wide range of modelling studies. In general, the available evidence to date is not inconsistent with this understanding. Our understanding of the climate system, and its sensitivity to increased concentrations of atmospheric greenhouse gases, would have to be sadly adrift for us to dismiss the possibility of climate change due to an enhanced greenhouse effect resulting principally from man's activities.

It has to be conceded, however, that many scientific uncertainties exist which make prediction of the nature, magnitude and timing of climate change, particularly at the regional and smaller scales, unreliable at present. Indeed, current modelling studies give estimates only to within a factor of about two for the global average temperature increase resulting from a given greenhouse-gas scenario.

THE EFFECTS OF AN ENHANCED GREENHOUSE EFFECT

The implications of a global warming because of a build up of atmospheric greenhouse gases could be serious and far-reaching, both environmentally and economically. They will provide the greatest changes experienced since the last Ice Age. Indeed, the rate of change may well be unique, with current predictions indicating a rate of warming some 10–60 times faster than previously occurring at the start and end of glacial periods. Much has been written about the possibilities of global and regional changes in temperature and rainfall patterns, the melting of the polar ice caps, sea-level rise, and the concomitant effects on vegetation and freshwater systems. Climatic processes, however, are extremely complex. While computer predictions indicate the possibility of a global warming of between $1.5 - 4.5°C$, with an expected doubling of the concentration of greenhouse gases at some time between 2030 and 2100, the effects of such a warming will have marked regional variations.

This predicted temperature change should be contrasted with the natural changes which have occurred in the geologically recent past. Climate in Britain over the last million years has fluctuated between intense cold glacial periods and the temperature conditions similar to today. There is no reason to believe that this fluctuation of climate is over, although we have been in the present interglacial for the last 8 000 years. There have been some 17 glacial periods in the last 1.5 M years, during which the ambient temperature in mid-latitude regions decreased by some 9°C. The large amount of water retained in ice sheets lowered global sea level by 100 m or more and great ice sheets grew and spread south into Europe and North America. Climatic changes, important in human terms, if less striking in scale than the glacial-interglacial fluctuations, have occurred over the last 10 000 years and continue today. These include the cooling of the 16–18th Century, the 'Little Ice Age', when glaciers advanced and farming in uplands generally became difficult or impossible. The subsequent rise in relative sea level, although slight, is influencing coastal sedimentation and putting pressure on sea defences.

CONCLUSION

While there is general agreement in predicting a globally-averaged temperature rise, its magnitude is estimated only to within a factor of about two for any given greenhouse-gas scenario and, in general, different models produce significantly different detailed regional changes in temperature and precipitation. At present, there are only a few broad indications of agreement at the regional scale between atmospheric general circulation models coupled to simplistic models of the ocean and sea-ice. The largest temperature increases occur over sea-ice and surrounding regions in winter. The overall average precipitation increases but the effect is not distributed uniformly over the globe. A general increase in winter precipitation in middle latitudes is indicated. Other climatic effects such as the frequency of extreme events and changing wind patterns can also be expected with a general temperature change.

Estimates of expected climate change by the middle of the next century depend not only on the assumptions made about climate sensitivity (as a result of complicated factors involving the thermal inertia of the oceans and feedback mechanisms involving atmospheric water vapour, clouds, surface interactions etc), but also on the assumptions that have to be made about future emissions of all the significant greenhouse gases. All the effects of climate change need not be deleterious, at least on a regional scale and in the short-term, although some local effects are likely to have a profound influence worldwide.

REFERENCE

Boyle, S & Ardill, J (1989) *The Greenhouse Effect*. New English Library, Hodder & Stoughton.

Bennett, R M (Ed) (1989) *The 'greenhouse effect' and UK agriculture*. CAS Paper 19. Reading: Centre for Agricultural Strategy.

2 The potential impact on agriculture of the 'greenhouse effect'

Martin Parry

INTRODUCTION

This paper first considers the array of methods currently used to assess the likely effects of climatic changes on agriculture. It then outlines the range of possible effects on agriculture in various parts of the World, before proceeding to consider likely impacts in the UK. It concludes with a summary of the changes in technology and policy that may comprise appropriate responses, either to mitigate the negative effects of climate change or take advantage of the positive ones.

METHODS OF IMPACT ASSESSMENT

Models

The most widely used approach in the assessment of impacts of climatic change is one that employs a hierarchy of models (see Figure 1). At the top of the hierarchy are models or 'scenarios' of climatic variation. These are used as inputs to biophysical models of first-order relationships (ie those between certain climatic variables and biophysical supply or demand). Outputs from these (for example, in the form of altered crop yields or yield probabilities) are used as inputs to economic models of second-order relationships at the enterprise level. These consider the effects, for example, of changes in farm-level production on farm incomes, farm purchases, etc. As a further step, economic models of higher-order relationships (for instance, those between farm profitability and regional employment or gross domestic product) can be employed to evaluate effects elsewhere in a region. This was the approach followed by the International Institute for Applied Systems

Figure 1
Types of model used and stages of analysis in the assessment of the impacts of climate change on agriculture by IIASA

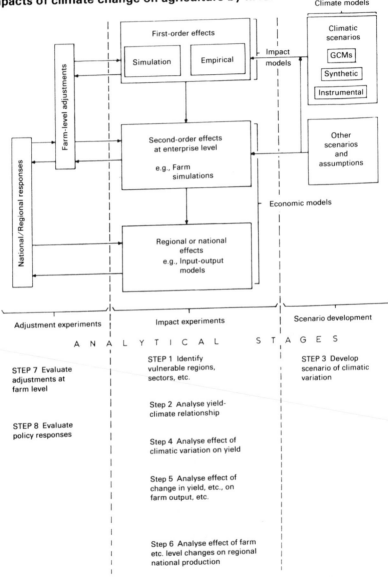

Source: Parry & Carter (1988).

Analysis (IIASA) in its case studies of impacts on agriculture (Parry et al, 1988a & 1988b). Ideally the effects of climatic variations are analysed in terms of their interactions with other physical systems, distinguishing between those in which the effects of a climatic variation are transmitted through other physical systems (eg by changes in soil structure, soil nutrients and soil erosion; by pests and diseases, etc), and those in which the effects of a climatic variation are themselves affected by other concurrent environmental trends such as groundwater pollution, soil nutrient depletion and so on.

Recent studies, such as that by IIASA and the US Environmental Protection Agency (EPA, 1988), have distinguished between, and tested, two types of response to climate impacts:

(i) adjustments at the enterprise level (which at the farm level might include changes of crops, increased irrigation, changes in fertilization, etc) and

(ii) policy responses at the regional, national and international level (see Figure 1).

Direct and adjoint methods

The scientific method most commonly adopted in climate impact assessment is the *direct method*, in which the analysis proceeds in a number of steps from a given climatic change to the estimated impacts (eg change in temperature ⇒ change in crop biomass productivity ⇒ change in forage level ⇒ change in carrying capacity ⇒ change in livestock production ⇒ change in meat and milk supply, etc). The analysis is thus conducted on the basis of the character of the climatic changes rather than their likely impacts. However, given the present uncertainties about changes of climate, particularly at the regional level, agricultural impact assessments have tended to adopt an alternative or *adjoint method*, considering first the varying sensitivities of different regions, sectors and farming systems to different types of climatic variation and thus identifying, *a priori*, points of especial vulnerability that should be the focus for study. The steps are illustrated in Figure 1. An advantage of this approach is that it can help identify sensitivities independently of state-of-the-art projections of future climate, employing a range of plausible scenarios both climatic and non-climatic in origin (Parry & Carter, 1984).

Climatic scenarios

Three methods have been used to characterise the altered climates expected under higher concentrations of greenhouse gases. Most widely used are the results of experiments with atmospheric general circulation models (GCMs), commonly for an equivalent doubling of atmospheric concentrations of CO_2. Some studies have made use of historical analogues of warmer conditions (such as the 1930s warm and dry period on the North

American Great Plains). Finally, it is possible to develop synthetic scenarios of possible future climates by adopting combinations of arbitrary changes in climatic variables (such as +1 and +2°C, +10% and −10% precipitation).

In the summary that follows the effects considered are those expected under climates simulated by GCMs for an equivalent 2 x CO_2 forcing. Five GCMs have been used, to date, in 2 x CO_2 experiments. There are quite wide differences between them in the magnitude of changes in temperature and precipitation but, more importantly for agriculture, there is very little agreement on the likely changes in regional patterns of precipitation.

TYPES OF EFFECT ON AGRICULTURE

To date, only three comprehensive assessments of the consequences of climate change for agriculture have been completed at the regional and national scale, and there has been none at the global level. National assessments have been undertaken in the US and Canada, and international regional case studies have been carried out by IIASA for the UN Environment Programme (EPA, 1988; Environment Canada, 1987; Parry et al, 1988a & 1988b). A number of countries have completed reviews of existing knowledge, as opposed to initiating new research, including the UK, Australia and New Zealand (DOE, 1988; Pearman 1988; J M Salinger, personal communication). The following is a summary of the types of effect on agriculture that emerge from these studies, rather than a description of them for each region.

It is useful to distinguish between two broad types of effect on agriculture – the fertilizing effect that increased atmospheric CO2 may have on plant growth, and the effect of changes in weather on crops, livestock, diseases, pests, weeds and soils.

The fertilizing effect of increased CO_2

Carbon dioxide in the atmosphere can enhance plant growth in a number of ways. It can increase the rate of photosynthesis, leading to greater leaf expansion and a larger canopy, and it can reduce water losses from crop plants - a beneficial effect where drought is a problem.

The effects are much more pronounced, however, in some crops than others. C3 crops, such as wheat, barley, rice and potatoes, respond vigorously to CO_2 enhancement. But C4 crops, such as maize, sorghum and sugar cane, do not. Crops in central and northern Europe thus stand to gain, although the outlook is not so good in much of Africa where maize, sorghum, sugar cane and millet are staple crops.

In addition, it should be noted that in north-west Europe the more troublesome weeds for arable farming are all C3 species and should benefit from CO_2 enhancement. Although little experimental evidence is available, it is likely that they could become more troublesome if C4 crops such as maize are cultivated widely.

More research is needed before we can say how much yield increase will occur in crops, but for a doubling of CO_2 it could be as much as 40% for wheat and barley (Cure, 1985). This figure should be approximately halved for effects that might occur by about 2030 (the estimated time at which increases in greenhouse gases would have an effect equivalent to a doubling of CO_2), because increases in CO_2 account for only about half of estimated greenhouse-gas forcing. There are also some negative aspects to the 'direct' effects of CO_2– the food quality of plants tends to deteriorate as carbon dioxide levels increase. Leaves become richer in carbon and poorer in nitrogen. Pests feeding off these leaves may thus need to consume more to gain their required nitrogen nutrient levels (Oechel & Strain, 1985). Moreover, if plants grow more quickly they may need more fertilizer, and if rainfall increases while plants require less moisture, that might mean more run-off, more erosion of the soil and more leaching-out of soil nutrients.

Effects of changes in weather

The effects through changes of climate and weather are less easy to determine because they will continue to vary greatly from year to year and from region to region, and there is great uncertainty about these future temporal and spatial patterns of climate. Because of this, most current estimates are for average (equilibrium) conditions that might prevail under an increase in greenhouse gases equivalent to a doubling of atmospheric CO_2. The following summary considers, initially, first-order (biophysical) impacts and, secondly, higher-order effects on the economy.

First-order effects

(i) *Changes in length of growing season and period of crop growth.*
Two of the major implications of CO_2-induced temperature changes for the growth of agricultural crops at present cultivated in cool temperate and cold regions are, first, a lengthening of the potential growing season and, second, an increase in plant growth rates and thus a shortening of the required growing period. For example, in southern Saskatchewan under the $2 \times CO_2$ scenario developed by the Goddard Institute for Space Studies (GISS) GCM, with mean May-August temperatures increased by about 3.5°C, the growing season is lengthened by 4-9 weeks, while the estimated maturation period for current varieties of spring wheat is reduced by 4-14 days (Williams *et al*, 1988). Broadly similar increases in the growing season are indicated for similar high-latitude locations, such as Scandinavia, central USSR and northern Japan (Parry *et al*, 1988) implying increases in production potential in the regions.

At lower latitudes, particularly where growing seasons are

determined by rainfall, it is much less clear what the consequences may be. There are some indications that rainfall may decrease in the Mediterranean region, the southern US and in some other semi-arid regions, which would, *ceteris paribus*, lead to shortened crop growing seasons (EPA, 1988; Jager, 1988).

(ii) *Changes in mean crop yield.*

In cool temperate and cold regions yields of most crops can be expected to increase with increasing temperature, except where moisture is a limiting factor. Under these conditions the low-temperature constraints on achieving potential yields are reduced. However, the temperature increases estimated at high latitudes are in some cases so great that existing, often quick-maturing, crop cultivars are ill-adapted to the longer and more intense growing season and to the variability about the higher mean temperatures. As a result, mean yield levels indicated by recent studies are usually no greater (and frequently lower) than those obtained during anomalously warm periods at the present day (Parry & Carter, 1988).

Some crops can be expected to perform better than others. For example, under the 2 x CO_2 GISS scenario, winter wheat would probably give higher yields than spring cereals in Saskatchewan (Williams *et al*, 1988) and in the central (Moscow) region of the USSR. Also, in the latter region, crops with greater thermal requirements such as maize would show a greater increase in yield than cool-region crops such as potatoes and oats (Pitovranov *et al*, 1988). The differences in yield between various crops can thus be expected to alter. This will affect the relative profitability of different crops and thus the extent to which they are grown in different regions.

In the United States, there are indications of decreases in yields of wheat, maize and soya under a 2 x CO_2 climate (EPA, 1988). For wheat, these decreases may be partly compensated by the direct, fertilizing effect of CO_2. Overall, however, there are significant decreases in the productive potential of staple food grains under the 2 x CO_2 climatic scenarios derived from a variety of GCM experiments.

In Australia, yields of winter wheat may be reduced if there is a decrease in winter rainfall, particularly in marginal growing areas such as the south-west of Western Australia (Pearman, 1988).

(iii) *Spatial shifts of agricultural potential.*

The changes in agricultural potential described in the preceding pages imply that climatic change is likely to bring about a spatial shift of crop potential. Areas which are, under present climatic conditions, judged to be most suited to a given crop or combination of crops or to a specified level of management will change location. In its simplest form this kind of shift can be seen as a shift in limits of the cultivable area. For example, large-scale climate-related shifts of potential for maize and wheat have been investigated in North America (Blasing & Solomon, 1983; Rosenzweig, 1985).

One potentially useful method of interpreting future climatic scenarios and their likely impact is to identify *analogue regions*, which have a present-day climate that is analogous to the future climate estimated for a study area. Analogue regions of this kind are shown in Figure 2, based upon changes in temperature and precipitation assumed under the GISS $2 \times CO_2$ scenario. Note that the figure was constructed using information from only one or two meterological stations in each case study area, and is designed merely to be illustrative.

This analogue approach is useful in illustrating the magnitude of climatic change within a region in terms of the present-day differences between regions. For example, Iceland's climate under the GISS $2 \times CO_2$ scenario is similar to the climate of northern Britain today. Moreover, the present-day farming types in analogue regions are a useful indicator of the adaptive strategies likely to be required to re-tune agriculture to altered climatic resources. For example, rice varieties at present grown in central Japan, which was identified as an appropriate regional analogue for the GISS $2 \times CO_2$ scenario in northern Japan (Hokkaido) were used in adjustment experiments with crop simulations for Hokkaido to evaluate their adoption as an appropriate adaptive response (Yoshino *et al*, 1988).

Figure 2

Present-day regional analogues of the GISS $2 \times CO_2$ climate

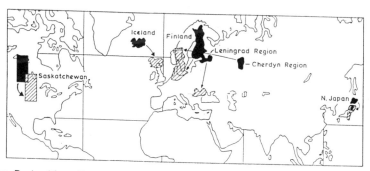

Source: Derived from Parry & Carter (1988)

Higher-order effects of climatic variations on agriculture

Several types of higher-order effect at the farm, regional and national level arise directly from the first-order effects summarised above.

(i) *Effects on farm profitability.*

These are difficult to assess because their estimation assumes a

33

knowledge of any change in the costs of inputs (see Ketturen *et al*, 1988 and Williams *et al*, 1988 for examples of such assessments in Finland and Saskatchewan respectively).

(ii) *Effects on regional production costs.*
Changes of yield may also affect production costs, particularly in centrally-planned economies where regional production targets are fixed and where levels of input are often adjusted to counter weather-related variations of yield (see Pitovranov *et al*, 1988).

(iii) *Effects on regional and national food production.*
As yields are altered by differing amounts according to crop type, soil type, level of input and type of management, the aggregate effect on regional or national food production is not easy to evaluate. As a result, it has thus far been possible only to provide model-based estimates for single crops (eg Williams *et al*, 1988; Yoshino *et al*, 1988).

Few generalisations can yet be made about likely effects on global food supply. However, it is quite possible that warming will increase output potential at high latitudes in the northern hemisphere – in regions where current farm output is encouraged by heavy state subsidies. Without large-scale reductions in this support, it is likely that surplus production would increase in these areas under a warmer climate.

Overall, it is quite possible that climatic change could alter the geographical pattern of main producing regions to the world food market. It is not possible at present, however, to say how this pattern might change, except that (in the most general sense) warming may enhance agricultural potential in high latitude and mid-latitude maritime regions and reduce potential in mid- and low-latitude continental regions. There have been estimates that, worldwide, average agricultural production costs could increase by 10–20% (Schelling, 1983), though this has been disputed (Crosson, 1989).

POTENTIAL IMPACTS IN THE UK

At the level of the UK, only the most generalised changes can reasonably be estimated, and even these are unclear. In the absence of more precise information it may be reasonable, for the present, to assume that changes in average annual temperatures in the UK will broadly follow those best estimates of changes in global average temperatures. Estimations for greenhouse-gas emissions that are assumed to continue to increase along their present path, suggest an increase of about 0.5°C by 2000–2010, about 1.5°C by 2020–2050 and about 3°C by 2050–2100+, with warming in the UK possibly more pronounced in winter than summer. These estimates have been made by the Climatic Research Unit at the University of East Anglia (Wigley, 1989). The ranges in the timing of temperature increases given here reflect uncertainties about how the climate will actually respond.

Possible changes in rainfall in the UK are much less clear. In the south and east there may be less summer rainfall and more winter rainfall, while in the north and west, both winter and summer rainfall could increase (DOE, 1988). There is a possibility that, with higher temperatures, rainfall may be more in the form of convective thunderstorms.

Though we should not be complacent, particularly with the high degree of remaining uncertainty, the implications of these climatic changes for the UK do not seem as dramatic as for some other parts of the World, and are in many respects ones that offer opportunities to UK agriculture.

Effects from sea-level rise

Recent estimates of sea-level rises of as much as 7 m are probably greatly exaggerated. The present scientific consensus is around 0.2 m to 1.5 m by about 2030 (Jager, 1988). However, it may still cost the UK in the region of £5 000 M in new sea defences to protect against high tides and storm surges acting at the higher mean sea levels – and this would not protect against a rise in fresh groundwater levels, which could waterlog low-lying soils (Boorman et al, 1988). There is also the possibility of intrusion of saltwater into groundwater in coastal regions, and of saltwater backing up rivers and estuaries, both of which could reduce the availability of water for irrigation.

In general, the effects of sea-level rise on UK agriculture seem to be negative. But at least the expected rise will be roughly constant over the next few decades, and at a rate (probably about 10 – 15 cm per decade) that should allow time to devise means of minimising the damage. It is the potential effect of climate on UK agriculture that is likely to be either more damaging or more beneficial for UK farmers.

Effects from climate

Let us consider first the changes in *potential* for farming. The growing period could lengthen in northern Europe if average temperatures increased. Under a climate predicted by the UK Meterological Office GCM for an equivalent doubling of CO_2, the number of months with average temperatures above 5°C and rainfall exceeding half of potential evapotranspiration would exceed 9 throughout the UK, save for the extreme south-east, where the growing season in the future might be interrupted by moisture shortage during the summer (Figures 3 and 4). Yet in the Mediterranean, the growing season could shorten significantly due to warmer and drier conditions in spring and autumn. Seen in these simple terms, there is a shift of cropping potential from southern EC countries to northern EC countries.

Higher temperatures also imply that crops which are at present near their northern limit of cold tolerance in the UK would benefit, providing moisture remained in sufficient supply. Thus the temperature limit for the successful ripening of grain maize, which at present lies in the extreme south of England, would be re-located across central England with an average warming of 0.5°C, across northern England for +1.5°C and across northern Scotland for +3°C (Figure 5a). This is an average location for an average warmer climate, and is based on temperatures adjusted to sea level. Year-to-year variations could still be expected to occur around this average, just as they do now. For example, the temperature limit for maize in the summer of 1976 lay well north of its present normal position.

Figure 3
Length of growing period (months) under the present-day (1931–60) climate

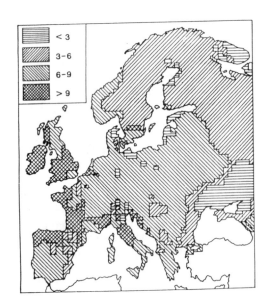

Source: Derived from Brouwer (1988).

Figure 4
Length of growing period (months) under the climate simulated by the UK Meterological Office GCM for a doubling of atmospheric CO_2 concentration

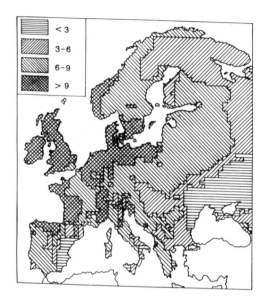

Source: Derived from Brouwer (1988).

The corresponding limit for silage maize can also be mapped according to its temperature requirements (Figure 5b). These are less demanding than those for grain maize, thus defining a present-day boundary across the (cooler) north of England. Again, the year-to-year variations around this average can be quite significant, illustrated here by the contrast between a warm year (1976) and a cool year (1962). Indeed, the scale of shift of such limits from the warmest to the coolest years in the past 30 years, is broadly similar to that expected to occur under a 2 to 3°C warming. Any future warmer climate would also have embedded within it the year-to-year variations of growing season that we experience now, but whether the range of these variations will be similar to the range experienced today is uncertain. This temperature limitation is, of course, only one of several limitations placed on maize growing in the UK.

The pattern of rainfall is also likely to change and while temperature and rainfall may alter, daylength (which is also important) will not. Several crops are constrained in the UK as much by lack of sunshine and by quite high levels of air humidity as by temperature. Sunflowers, for example, are restricted at present to the extreme south of England, and even here there is a problem of mildew before the seedhead is fully ripe. But whatever remain

Figure 5
Hypothetical limits for successful ripening of (a) grain maize and (b) silage maize, based on temperature[1]

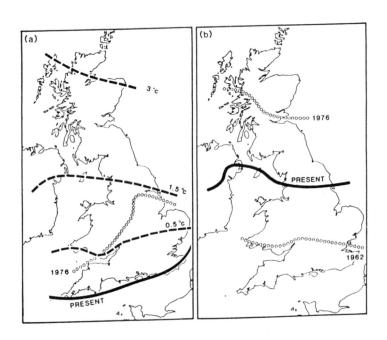

1 Grain maize requirement: 850 degree days above a base temperature of 10°C.
   Silage maize requirement: 1460 degree days above a base temperature of 6°C.
   Mean limits (solid lines) are representative of lowland conditions, based on temperature data from 78 stations for the period 1951–80. Limits for individual years (open circles) and for adjustments in mean temperature (broken lines) are also shown.

the other constraints on sunflower growth, their temperature limit may be re-located about 500 km further north under a climate that is 1.5°C warmer than it is at present. In summary it seems that such limits of temperature shift about 300 km northwards in the UK for each 1°C rise in mean annual temperature.

Whether a northward shift of crops will actually occur is a matter of how agriculture might respond to changes in potential, and that will be discussed later. But it remains a possibility that, if farmers respond simply to changes in climate, fields of grain maize and sunflowers (which are a common sight in France not more than 100 km south of the English Channel) could be a feature of southern England in the future.

However, while higher temperatures might extend the potential range of crops in the UK, they would tend to decrease yields of some crops in the present core production areas. For example, yields of current varieties of winter wheat in south-east England might be expected to decrease in the absence of CO_2 fertilization, and the positive effects of CO_2 could be cancelled out by temperature increases of above 4°C (Squire & Unsworth, 1988).

Much would depend on changes in rainfall in the UK, not only in the annual average amount but in its distribution throughout the year, and we know little about how this might change. However, we do know that relatively small changes in rainfall could affect the map of types of farming quite substantially. To illustrate, the broad distinction between the arable east and pastoral west of England partly stems from differences in rainfall receipt between east and west. Very approximately the line of 780 mm per year divides the regions having more or less than 40% of farmland under cereals (Davidson & Sturgess, 1978). A 20% decrease in annual rainfall, with the same seasonal pattern and regional distribution as now, would shift that 780 mm line up to 100 km westwards. Would that imply a westward extension of arable farming? Conversely, would an increase in rainfall lead to an eastward shift of land-use belts? The reality of this situation would be greatly complicated by other effects, for example by effects on the availability of water for irrigation in the east and on the existing market for meat and cereals. But the suggestion is that quite small changes in climate could substantially alter the pattern of agricultural potential. Again, we should stress that how UK farmers respond to such changes in potential is wholly another matter.

What of the possible changes in the uplands of Britain? A 3°C rise in temperature implies a rise in the potential limit to cultivation of about 500 m (1640 ft) (Squire & Unsworth, 1988). Thus where excessive rainfall and exposure did not continue to restrict farming, there might be increased opportunity for cropping in the uplands. Probably more important would be the extension of the grazing season by one or two weeks in both spring and autumn, making it more profitable to improve and maintain upland grassland, and higher temperatures could reduce the tendency for sedge and other rough grasses to invade improved land, making it easier to maintain. No figures are yet available for the increases in carrying capacity in the UK uplands, but recent work in Iceland indicates that, under a $2 \times CO_2$ warming of 4°C, the carrying capacity of improved grassland for sheep increases three and a half times and of unimproved rangeland increases two-thirds (Bergthorsson et al, 1988).

In reality, the future of agriculture in the UK will depend very much on changes elsewhere, particularly in the present breadbasket areas of the World. There are indications that higher temperatures and reduced moisture on the US Great Plains and the Canadian prairies, as a result of greenhouse warming, could significantly reduce production potential in North America. We should not rule out the possibility, then, of northern and central Europe increasing its role as a producer to the world food market.

Effects on water, soils, diseases and pests
Before considering the responses that farmers might make to these changes in potential, it is important to consider the concurrent effects that changes in climate will have indirectly on crops and livestock, through changes in water for irrigation, changes in soils, and changes in the rate of losses to diseases, pests and weeds.

In south-east England, in order to offset increased evapotranspiration under a 3°C warming, it is estimated that rainfall would need to increase by 10% if shortage of water for use in agriculture were to be avoided (Beran & Arnell, 1989). The increased costs of water that might result could affect the amount of water not only used in irrigation, but also in spraying and in washing fruit and vegetables. The cost of construction of irrigation systems (in the order of £1 000–£3 000 per hectare) could be one factor encouraging the westward and northward shift of cropping patterns. Reduced run-off in dry areas could reduce the dilution of waste, particularly of pesticide residues, with effects on toxicity levels of streams and thus on wildlife. In the uplands increased winter rainfall could increase leaching and reduce the pH of soils, and thus increase risk of flood and erosion.

Effects on soils depend much on the future seasonal pattern and intensity of rainfall, about which we know very little at present. An increase in thundershowers might increase run-off, thus increasing flooding and soil wash. But it also might reduce percolation, thus decreasing the amount of water available for agriculture. Increased rainfall could increase the mineralisation of organic nitrates, allowing extra plant uptake, but it could also increase leaching downwards of soil nutrients. In any case, quite small changes in rainfall could require sensitive alterations to the drainage of soils.

We can only guess at the implications for weeds, diseases and pests. Warmer winters would extend the growing season of some weeds. For example, corn marigold which flourishes in warmer and damper weather, could become more of a problem. In the south of England scrubby, drought-resistant species (which already have a toe-hold in southern Britain) could increase their range (Grime & Callaghan, 1988).

Diseases which tend to break out more frequently in warm, damp conditions could also increase (such as rust *(Puccinia graminis)*, take-all *(Gaeumannomyces graminis)* and *Rynchosporium* in cereals, and *Rhizomania* in sugar beet).

Warmer winters could also increase the over-wintering of pests, and increase their range. This could affect populations of aphids, pollen beetles (which are a pest on oilseed rape) and slugs.

In summary, some of the benefits of warmer and drier growing seasons in the southern UK, and of warmer and wetter growing seasons in the northern UK, might well be offset by increased losses to weeds, diseases and pests.

POSSIBLE RESPONSES IN AGRICULTURE

While there are many uncertainties about how our climate will change in the future, there is one relative certainty about modern agriculture and today's farmers – it is that they have shown themselves capable in the recent past of adapting to a very wide range of conditions, both economic and environmental. The question, then, is not so much, 'can UK agriculture adapt to the greenhouse effect?' but 'what kind of adaptations would be most appropriate, and how can scientific research and government policy best help this process?'

Firstly, many of the smaller changes in temperature and rainfall might be accommodated by adjustments to the timing of farming operations. For example, were the number of rainfall days to increase between (say) mid-February and mid-April (during the period when wet days can restrict the drilling of spring crops and the application of herbicides and nitrogen), it might be possible to shift these operations forward by one or two weeks. Advantage could thus be taken of a longer and warmer growing season that would allow harvest of cereals in mid- to late June rather than July.

Indeed, earlier maturation might be necessary in the south and east of England (if increases in temperature coincided with little or no increase in summer rainfall), in order to avoid losses from mid-summer drought. However, earlier emergence of the crop could make it more prone to damage from late frosts (if these were to occur with undiminished frequency). A switch to some Mediterranean wheat varieties which are more resistant to late season frosts might be appropriate if they yielded well under longer daylengths.

Any change in the number of workdays involved in ploughing, drilling, spraying or fertilizing due to changes in climate would alter the costs of operations quite substantially. Once more, the number of raindays is important here – and again we know little at present about how these may alter.

Changes in the pattern of weather events may bring new uncertainties to the task of deciding when to undertake given operations. While potential yields may not be diminished (and may even be enhanced) the uncertainties about the cost of obtaining such yields may increase.

Secondly, in addition to changes in the timing of operations, there could occur a shift from spring to winter varieties of cereals, in order to avoid a higher risk of moisture shortage in the early summer, and to take advantage of a prolonged growing season in the autumn and an earlier onset of growth in the spring.

Thirdly, it may make sense to switch to varieties of crops that have a longer or more intense growing season requirement than our present ones. This would be particularly beneficial where varieties developed for growing at present near their northern limit are able to mature only at some loss of quantity or quality of grain.

Fourthly, we can expect farmers in the UK to consider switching to new crops which have higher thermal requirements and are at present perhaps grown in the south of Britain or in central and southern France. Sunflowers could become a more profitable crop, in addition to grain maize, and perhaps even soya (which is at present grown in northern Italy). Navy beans, also grown in northern Italy and for which the UK imports all its needs at present, might also be cultivable under a climate that could occur in southern England within the next 50 – 100 years.

Of course, any changes in the allocation of land to different crops would be influenced as much by changes in the potential for cropping elsewhere. If drier and warmer conditions obtained in Europe south of the English Channel, with reduced potential for the profitable farming of maize, sunflowers, soya, etc, then this might well increase the competitiveness of such crops for farmland in the UK.

In the uplands of Britain, it might not be too far-fetched to imagine that the increased productivity of improved grassland, together with decreased productivity further south in Europe, could act as a spur to improvement of rough grazings. Due to higher temperatures and the direct fertilizing effect of CO_2, trees (both conifers and broadleaved) can be expected to grow faster, and do better at higher altitudes than they do now (unless windspeeds increase) (Cannell et al, 1988). Together, these two enterprises could substantially increase demand for the uplands, increasing competition for land at present used for water catchment (which might itself need to be increased) and for wildlife and recreation.

Because these types of response will be interwoven in an incredibly complex way, it is probably not profitable to try to 'second-guess' them in detail. We need only recall, for example, that by 2030 (the estimated CO_2

doubling equivalent time for greenhouse gases) the World's population will also have nearly doubled from its present levels, and this could well alter the structure of demand and prices for food. These should not, however, be taken to imply that we should do nothing.

CONCLUSION

It is clear that we need to know much more about a number of aspects of likely changes in climate, particularly:

(i) what is likely to happen to the weather at the regional and local (rather than global) scale?;

(ii) how may rainfall alter, not simply on an average annual basis, but from season to season within the year? and

(iii) at what rate is the climate likely to change?

At the same time we need to know more about how quickly agriculture can adapt to the kinds of climate changes we may experience, and how we can assist in that adaptation. What, for example, is the potential for adopting crop varieties at present grown elsewhere? Or should we be thinking of developing new varieties now, since these may take about 10 years to develop and adopt? And what may be the cost of re-structuring agriculture (for example, what would be the cost of increasing irrigation to maintain in south-east England the kind of farming we see today, as against the cost of altering the type of farming there)?

These questions require several years more investigation before sufficiently detailed answers are likely to be available. It is probably unwise, therefore, to adopt a 'wait-and-see' attitude, particularly if there are disagreeable time lags in the climate system which imply that we are, even now, committed to some significant amount of climate change, and that the amount of change to which we will have to adapt will increase year by year the longer we delay an effort to reduce emissions of greenhouse gases. This suggests that, while continuing to pursue the scientific research to narrow the area of uncertainty about the greenhouse effect, we should also start thinking about the global agreements needed soon to reduce fossil fuel burning, improve efficiency in energy use and slow down the rate of deforestation.

Many of these policies of response would themselves have implications for agriculture in the future – such as policies to encourage afforestation in developed countries as a means of retrieving carbon from the atmosphere and storing it in trees, or encouraging the growing of crops that can be used in the production of alcohol as a substitute fuel for coal, oil and natural gas, or increasing the price of fuel to the consumer in order to reduce fuel consumption. (The latter could significantly increase the costs of fertilizers for agriculture.) The indications are that these policies will start to emerge within the next 4 or 5 years rather than 4 or 5 decades. Both the policies and the climate changes are likely to bring opportunities as well as costs for agriculture. It will be important to evaluate these opportunities and costs carefully, so that agriculture in the UK can respond in the most appropriate way.

REFERENCES

Beran, M A & Arnell, N W (1989) *Effect of climatic change on quantitative aspects of United Kingdom Water Resources*. Contract Report to the Department of the Environment Water Directorate. Wallingford, Institute of Hydrology.

Bergthorsson, P, Bjornsson, H, Dyrmundsson, O, Gudmundsson, B, Helgadottir, A & Jonmundsson, J V (1988) The effect of climatic variations on agriculture in Iceland. In: Parry, M L, Carter, T N & Konijn, N J (Eds) *The impact of climatic variations on agriculture Volume 1. Assessments in cool temperate and cold regions*. Kluwer, Dordrecht, The Netherlands.

Blasing, T J & Soloman, A M (1983) *Response of the North American Corn Belt to climatic warming*. DOE/NBB-004. Prepared for the US Department of Energy, Office of Energy Research, CO_2 Research Division, Washington, D.C.

Boorman, L A, Goss-Custard, J & McGrorty, S (1988) *Ecological effects of climatic change: effects of sea level rise on coastal ecosystems of conservation and amenity interest in the UK*. Contract Report to the Department of the Environment. Abbots Ripton, Institute of Terrestrial Ecology.

Brouwer, F M (1988) *Determination of broad-scale landuse changes by climate and soils*. Working Paper WP-88-007. Laxenburg, Austria, International Institute for Applied Systems Analysis.

Cannell, M G R, Grace, J & Booth, A (1988) *Effects of changes in temperature and rainfall on trees and forests in the UK*. Contract Report to the Department of the Environment. Institute of Terrestrial Ecology, Bush Estate, Penicuik, Midlothian.

Crosson, P (1987) *Climate change and mid-latitude agriculture*. Paper given at the Workshop on Developing Policies for Responding to Climate Change, September 28-October 2, Villach, Austria.

Cure, J D (1985) Carbon dioxide doubling responses: a crop survey. In: Strain B R & Cure, J D (Eds) *Direct Effects of Increasing Carbon Dioxide on Vegetation*. DOE/ER-0238, Washington, D.C. United States Department of Energy.

Davidson, J G & Sturgess, I M (1978) *Cereals 1971-1977, Agricultural Enterprise Studies in England and Wales, Economic Report No. 47*. Department of Land Economy, University of Cambridge, Agricultural Economics Unit.

DOE (1988) *Possible impacts of climate change on the natural environment in the United Kingdom*. London, United Kingdom Department of Environment.

Environment Canada (1987) *Canadian Climate Impacts Program*. CCD 870-01, Downsview, Ontario.

EPA (1988) *The potential effects of global climate change on the United States*. Executive Summary, Draft Report to Congress, Office of Policy, Planning and Evaluation, United States Environmental Protection Agency, Washington, D.C.

Grime, J P & Callaghan, T V (1988) *Direct and indirect effects of climatic change on plant species, ecosystems and processes of conservation and amenity interest*. Contract Report to the Department of the Environment, Unit of Comparative Plant Ecology, University of Sheffield.

Jager, J (1988) *Developing policies for responding to climatic change*. Report of two international workshops held in 1987 (Villach, Austria and Bellagio, Italy), Environmental Defense Fund, Washington, D.C.

Kettunen, L, Mukula, J, Pogjonen, V, Rantanen, O & Varjo, U (1988) The effects of climatic variations on agriculture in Finland. In: Parry, M L, Carter, T R & Konijn, N T (Eds) *The impact of climatic variations on agriculture. Volume 1. Assessments in cool temperate and cold regions*. Kluwer, Dordrecht, The Netherlands.

Oechel, W C & Strain, B R (1985) Native species responses to increasing atmospheric carbon dioxide concentrations. In: Strain, B R & Cure, J D (Eds) *Direct Effects of Increasing Carbon Dioxide on Vegetation*. United States Department of Energy, DOE/ER-0238, Washington, D.C.

Parry, M L & Carter, T R (Eds) (1984) *Assessing the impact of climatic change in cold regions*. Summary Report SR-84-1, Laxenburg, Austria. International Institute for Applied Systems Analysis.

Parry, M L & Carter, T R (1988) The assessment of effects of climatic variations on agriculture: Aims, methods and summary of results. In: Parry, M L, Carter, T R & Konijn, N J (Eds) *The impact of climatic variations on agriculture. Volume 1. Assessments in cool temperate and cold regions*. Kluwer, Dordrecht, The Netherlands.

Parry, M L, Carter, T R, & Konijn, N T (Eds) (1988a) *The impact of climatic variations on agriculture. Volume 1. Assessments in cool temperate and cold regions*. Kluwer, Dordrecht, The Netherlands.

Parry, M L, Carter, T R & Konijn, N T (Eds) (1988b) *The impact of climatic variations on agriculture. Volume 2. Assessments in semi-arid regions*. Kluwer, Dordrecht, The Netherlands.

Parry, M L, Carter, T L & Porter, J H (1989) The Greenhouse Effect and the future of UK agriculture. *Journal of the Royal Agricultural Society of England* (forthcoming).

Parry, M L & Carter, T R (1989) An assessment of the effects of climatic change on agriculture. *Climatic Change* (forthcoming).

Pearman, G I (Ed) (1988) *Greenhouse: Planning for climatic change*. Brill, Leiden, The Netherlands.

Pitovranov, S E, Iakimets, V N, Kiselev, V I, & Sirotenko, O D (1988) The effects of climatic variations on agriculture in the Subarctic Zone of the USSR. In: Parry, M L, Carter, T R & Konijn N T (Eds) *The impact of climatic variations on agriculture. Volume 1. Assessments in cool temperate and cold regions*. Kluwer, Dordrecht, The Netherlands.

Rosenzweig, C (1985) Potential CO_2-induced effects on North American wheat producing regions. *Climatic Change*, **7**, 367–389.

Schelling, T (1983) Climate change: Implications for welfare and policy In: *Changing climate: Report of the Carbon Dioxide Assessment Committee*. Washington, D.C, National Academy of Sciences.

Squire, G R & Unsworth, M H (1988) *Effects of CO_2 and climatic change on agriculture*. Contract Report to the Department of the Environment. Sutton Bonington, UK, University of Nottingham.

Wigley, T M L (1989) *The Greenhouse Effect: Scientific assessment of climatic change*. Lecture presented at the Prime Minister's Seminar on Global Climate, 12 Downing Street, London, 26 April 1989.

Williams, G D V, Fautley, R A, Jones, K H, Stewart, R B & Wheaton, E E (1988) Estimating effects of climatic change on agriculture in Saskatchewan, Canada. In: Parry, M L, Carter, T R & Konijn, N T (Eds) *The impact of climatic variations on agriculture. Volume 1. Assessments in cool temperate and cold regions*. Kluwer, Dordrecht, The Netherlands.

Yoshino, M, Horie, T, Seino, H, Tsujii, H, Uchijima, T & Uchijima, Z (1988) The effect of climatic variations on agriculture in Japan. In: Parry, M L, Carter, T R & Konijn, (Eds) *The impact of climatic variations on agriculture. Volume 1. Assessments in cool temperate and cold regions*. Kluwer, Dordrecht, The Netherlands.

Bennett, R M (Ed) (1989) *The 'greenhouse effect' and UK agriculture*. CAS Paper 19. Reading: Centre for Agricultural Strategy.

3 The 'greenhouse effect' and crop production in the UK

Harold Woolhouse

INTRODUCTION

If one were to follow Wittgenstein's dictum — 'whereof we do not know, thereof we cannot speak' — this paper would not be given. It cannot be emphasised too heavily that uncertainty surrounds the prediction of the build up of greenhouse gases, the overall impact of the gases on climate forcing, the impact on local circulation patterns in the atmosphere and attendant effects on wind and rainfall, and the impact of these physical phenomena on the biota.

For the purposes of this paper I shall assume a doubling of CO_2 concentration to around 600 ppmv by the year 2040, with attendant increases in anthropogenic greenhouse gases sufficient to produce a mean global warming (a concept of very limited value) of around 1.5°C.

I would defend the gas increase predictions on the general grounds that over half of the global fossil fuel reserves lie in India, China and the Soviet Union (Ausubel, 1983), as shown in Table 1, and there is bound to be exploitation of these reserves if standards of living are to be raised in these countries, since energy use per caput rises in linear relation to increases in standard of living (Claassen & Girifalco, 1986), as illustrated by Figure 1.

It is also important to emphasise that in the ocean of speculation surrounding the greenhouse effect, many of the scenarios owe as much to the psychological disposition of the protagonists, as to anything concerned with science (Isdo, 1984).

Table 1
Approximate world distribution of coal reserves (Gt)[1]

US	130	UK	30	Yugoslavia	6
USSR	120	Australia	20	GDR	5
China	70	FRG	20	Indonesia	4
		Poland	20	Czechoslovakia	2
		South Africa	20	Canada	2
		India	10	Botswana	2
				Swaziland	1
				Bulgaria	1

1 Gt = 10^9 tonnes. Deposits larger than 1 Gt listed.
  (These account for about 460 Gt out of 485 Gt world total).

Source: Derived from Ausubel (1983).

Figure 1
Relationship between energy consumption and standard of living

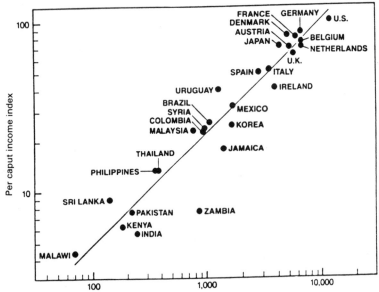

Source: Derived from Claassen & Girifalco (1986).

THE GREENHOUSE EFFECT AND RESEARCH ON CROP PRODUCTION

Implications of the greenhouse effect for agricultural production have been widely discussed and reviewed, see Smit *et al* (1988). If one could imagine an increase to 600 ppmv of CO_2 in isolation from other climatic consequences, then the broad conclusion is that crop production would increase by 30–40% (Kimball, 1983). This prediction is based on CO_2 enrichment experiments coupled with our understanding of the biochemistry and physiology of photosynthesis, in which a key reaction has been identified where CO_2 and O_2 compete at the enzyme site of CO_2 fixation (Bowes & Ogren, 1972).

Many studies have been carried out in order to examine the effects of CO_2 on crop yield. The majority of the experiments have been conducted in controlled environment rooms, on account of the expense and technical difficulty of CO_2 enrichment under field conditions. In consequence, the predictions arising from such work are based on extrapolation from growthroom to field conditions. Protagonists of the controlled environment approach argue that our ability to control such variables as nutrient availability, temperature, vapour pressure deficit of the air, CO_2 concentration and soil water potential, allows the provision of data for accurate predictive models. There is little doubt that growthroom studies enable the manipulation of individual variables and can serve to highlight potentially important factors, but they cannot be readily applied to the detailed characterisation of effects on over-wintering, rooting behaviour, susceptibility to pests and diseases, canopy structure and droughting parameters or the changes in the competitive ability relative to that of the weed population. How can this be remedied?

THE NEED FOR NEW EXPERIMENTAL APPROACHES

It would seem that if we are to get really worthwhile predictions of crop responses, there will have to be a substantial measure of field experimentation to complement the growthroom work. The greatest difficulties arise over the provision of sustained supplies of CO_2 and heat for application on a field scale. This could be achieved by developing methods and equipment for scrubbing not only SO_2 but also oxides of nitrogen from the exhaust systems of power stations, and piping the CO_2 enriched air to nearby crop sites. Waste heat in the form of warm water could be provided from the same source. Experimental facilities could thus be provided for investigation of the seasonal impact of CO_2 enrichment and its interaction with a range of climatic variables and the attendant impact on growth, pest and disease incidence, harvest index, total yields and crop quality. The AFRC Institute of Arable Crops Research has a good model for the growth of winter wheat under field conditions. Such models could be adapted to accommodate the data and generate predictions from experiments such as those recommended here.

It should not be overlooked that the results of such experimentation could point to drastic changes in our agriculture. There is suggestive evidence that increased CO_2 and warming may have greater effects on the yield of vegetative crops and pastures than on grains. If this were coupled with increased humidity-favouring disease incidence, it may push the national balance more towards animal than arable crop production. It is also possible that such conditions would favour increased forest production (Isdo, 1984).

IMPACT OF NEW TECHNOLOGY

One is frequently asked about the potential applicability of genetic engineering in accommodating to the impact of the greenhouse effect.

It seems unlikely that in the foreseeable future we shall be able to do much about photosynthesis *per se*. Under favourable conditions the process is about 30% efficient, which is close to the limits of thermodynamic prediction. By the same token it seems unlikely that we shall be able to improve on 2 billion years of natural selection to design a form of ribulose biphosphate carboxylase, the enzyme responsible for CO_2 fixation, which is resistant to the aforementioned effects of oxygen competition. At the higher levels of organisation, such as the partitioning of assimilates into storage products, the geometry of crop canopies and the stomatal responses of crops, there is a long way to go, but more cause for optimism. Thus, recent work on the isolation of genes controlling such attributes as starch synthesis (Martin, C, Smith, A & Bhattacharyya, M, personal communication), the use of transposon tagging for the isolation of genes controlling plant development and morphology (Coen *et al*, 1989) and the demonstration by Woodward (1987) of CO_2-dependent changes in stomatal frequency, suggest that the genetic manipulation of such attributes may be within reach. The prospects for profound modification of the thermal responses of crops are less encouraging, for here it seems probable that a large proportion of the genetic apparatus may need to be modified to achieve the integrated thermal adaptation of the whole plant (Woolhouse, 1988).

When one turns to field effects the situation is much more promising. Molecular biological approaches to stress responses such as temperature, drought, and salinity are already yielding results (eg Ougham & Howarth, 1988; Quarrie & Lister, 1988; Forster, 1988) and offer the prospect of genetic engineering of herbicide resistance, pest resistance using protease inhibitors and toxic proteins of bacterial origin, and, in the longer-term, the isolation and manipulation of genes for bacterial and fungal disease resistance (Woolhouse, 1987).

Thus, insofar as the greenhouse effect is likely to enhance the competitive abilities of some weed species, the over-wintering and abundance of some pests and predators, and the incidence of fungal and bacterial pathogens of plants, our ability to combat these deleterious factors by recourse to genetic engineering may well prove a factor in accommodating to some secondary consequences of the greenhouse effect.

CONCLUSION

The amount being said and written about the greenhouse effect far outweighs the observational and experimental work. More data for improvement of the global and local, atmosphere and ocean, circulation models are desperately needed. Crop physiology in Britain has been unwisely neglected in recent years – it needs a major cash injection to provide the new field experimental facilities that I have pointed to. The recently increased support for plant molecular biology may well prove timely, particularly if some of the effort is directed towards a much more thorough investigation of the genetic determinants of stress responses in plants.

REFERENCES

Ausubel, J H (1983) Can we assess the impact of climatic change? *Climatic Change*, **5**, 7–14.

Bowes, G & Ogren, W L (1972) O_2 inhibition and other properties of soyabean ribulose 1,5-diphosphate carboxylase. *Journal of Biological Chemistry*, **247**, 2171–76.

Claassen, R S & Girifalco, L A (1986) Materials for energy utilisation. *Scientific American*, **255**, (4), 84–92.

Coen, E, Robbins, T P, Almeida, J, Hudson, A & Carpenter, R (1989) Consequences and mechanisms of transposition in Antirrhinum majus. In: Berg, D E & Howe, M M, (Eds) Mobile DNA. *American Society for Microbiology*, 413–436.

Forster, B P (1988) *The introduction of salt tolerance into wheat.* AFRC Institute of Plant Science Research & John Innes Institute, Annual Report 1987, 14. Suffolk, UK: John Catt Ltd.

Isdo, S B (1984) A review of recent reports dealing with the Greenhouse Effect of atmospheric carbon dioxide. *Journal of the Air Pollution Control Association*, **34** (5), 553–555.

Kimball, B A (1983) Carbon dioxide and agricultural yield: an assemblage and analysis of 430 prior observations. *Agronomy Journal*, **75**, 779–788.

Ougham, H J & Howarth, C J (1988) Temperature shock proteins in plants. In: Long, S P & Woodward, F I (Eds) *Plants and Temperature*. Society for Experimental Biology Symposium, Company of Biologists, Cambridge, 42, 259–280.

Quarrie, S A & Lister, P G (1988) *Identification and characterisation of proteins synthesized rapidly during drought*. AFRC Institute of Plant Science Research and John Innes Institute Annual Report, 1988, 6–7 Suffolk, UK: John Catt Ltd.

Smit, B, Ludlow, L & Brklacich M (1988) Implications of a global climatic warming for agriculture: a review and appraisal. *Journal of Environmental Quality*, **17**, 4, 5190–527.

Woodward, F I (1987) Stomatal numbers are sensitive to increases in CO_2 from pre-industrial levels. *Nature*, **337**, 617–618.

Woolhouse, H W (1987) New plants and old problems. *Annals of Botany*, **60**, 4, 189–198.

Woolhouse, H W (1988) Problems and proposals for the understanding of temperature responses in plants. In: Long, S P & Woodward, F I (Eds) *Plants and Temperature*. Proceedings of the SEB Symposium No 42, Cambridge, Company of Biologists, 411–415.

Bennett, R M (Ed) (1989) *The 'greenhouse effect' and UK
agriculture*. CAS Paper 19. Reading: Centre for Agricultural
Strategy.

4 The 'greenhouse effect' and animal production in the UK

Peter Wilson

INTRODUCTION

Most of the definitive research work on the 'greenhouse effect' has been
done on plant growth and little on the specifics of livestock production. Much
of this paper, therefore, must perforce be speculative and based upon
numerous assumptions, few of which have been subjected to experimental
challenge.

ASSUMPTIONS AS TO CLIMATIC CHANGE

Most models of future climate change take the forcing term to be a doubling
of pre-Industrial Revolution levels of carbon dioxide to 540 ppm by the year
2050. Most models predict, for the UK as a whole, that mean temperatures
will rise by 3°C with an uncertainty (ie variation between models) of ±1.5°C.
This rise in temperature is seasonally dependant, with winter temperatures
being about 4°C, and summer temperatures about 2°C, higher.

The effect on rainfall, and humidity, is much less clear-cut. The various
models differ in predicting changes in precipitation but most agree that there
will be a change of the order of ±20% according to season and according to
region.

In general, the changes in mean temperature will be similar in effect to an
apparent southward shift in latitude of about 10°. Thus, north-east Scotland
will have a similar mean annual temperature to that of present day south-
west England, while the climate of the southern UK will come closer to that
of south-west France. More uncertainty surrounds the regional variation in
precipitation, with most models agreeing that the western parts

of the UK will retain their maritime influence, but that central, eastern and southern England will probably shift to a more semi-Mediterranean climate with drier conditions. Further north, northern England and Scotland will be warmer but not necessarily drier, and it is in these regions that the rainfall effects are most difficult to predict.

Changes to upland climates will be important as such regions are of great significance to ruminant livestock production patterns in the UK. The lapse rate of mean temperature adopted by the UK Meteorological Office is 6°C per km (Taylor, 1976), varying by about ±2°C per km, depending on air mass type, slope and aspect. Thus an average rise of 3°C by the year 2050 is equivalent to an effective reduction in altitude of about 500 m with consequences for the number of growing degree-days. However, due to the uncertainty regarding precipitation, the actual effect on total growing days could well be severely limited if significant areas of the UK experience hotter and drier summers with increased drought periods when plant growth is minimal or non-existent.

Because of the different water-holding capacities of soil types, the climatic changes summarised above will be greatly modified by soil and subsoil. Heavy clays and light sands will be most affected by significant shifts in precipitation, whilst more balanced deep loams will be less affected.

EFFECTS ON CROPS FOR LIVESTOCK FEED
Climatic change will affect the production of feed crops in several ways. These are:

(i)   the area of the particular crops grown;
(ii) the yield of these crops;
(iii) the timing of production with respect to livestock requirements;
(iv) the efficiency of harvest and storage;
(v)   product quality;
(vi) cost of animal feed production.

Some of the main factors are considered below.

Whether or not a crop can be grown in the UK depends primarily on whether there is a sufficiently long growing season, which is itself influenced firstly by temperature and secondly by the availability (or excess) of water. As weather changes from year to year it is less important to find out whether the crop will grow in an average year, but more important to assess the probability of success over a number of years. Possibly, failure in one year out of ten might be an appropriate acceptable level of risk.

A model has been constructed which estimates the potential increase in area for particular food crops (Russell, G, personal communication). The proportion of the UK for different feed crop uses was estimated on the basis of rules drawn up for success as shown in Table 1. Five scenarios were examined:

- (i) present climate;
- (ii) a temperature rise of 4°C in winter and 2°C in summer, no change in the after balance;
- (iii) temperature as in (ii), rainfall +20%;
- (iv) temperature as in (ii), rainfall and potential transpiration +20%;
- (v) temperature as in (ii), rainfall −20%.

The proportion of the UK for different land uses was then estimated by applying rules drawn up for the success of various enterprises (Table 1) to a database of information on soils and climate (Blackman *et al*, 1963; Francis, 1981; Smith, 1984) compiled for 115 random locations in the UK.

Table 1
Rules of success

Arable if $H_0 > 2750$ and soil 2 or 4 and $(R-PE) < 500$.

Silage maize *if* arable *and* $H_{10} > 900$.

Grain maize *if* arable *and* $H_{10} > 1000$.

Sunflower *if* arable *and* $H_{10} > 1000$.

Soya *if* arable *and* $H_{10} > 1215$.

Permanent grass if $H_0 > 2400$ and soil 1 or 2 or 4 and not arable.

Forest if $H_0 > 1859$ and soil 1 or 2 or 4 and not arable or permanent grass.

Rough grazing *if not* arable *or* permanent grass *or* forest.

Urban and other non-rural areas occupy 6% of the total.

Forest occupies 3% of the arable and permanent grass areas and 5% of the rough grazings.

Forest and urban areas remain constant.

Maize can be grown one year in four, sunflower and soya one in six.

Where H is the annual accumulated temperature above the subscripted base temperature; soil 1 = hill peat, 2 = mineral soil derived from glacial drift and 4 = *in situ* soil; $(R-PE)$ is the balance between precipitation and potential evaporation.

The predicted current areas were compared with the agricultural statistics (Central Statistical Office, 1988; Eurostat, 1988) and future areas were predicted (Table 2).

Table 2
Actual v predicted land use pattern

The area of land classes (x10³ha) currently (1987) and for five climatic change scenarios.

Land Class	1987	Scenario (i)	(ii)	(iii)	(iv)	(v)
Arable	7.0	7.7	7.7	5.8	6.9	9.0
Permanent grass	5.1	6.5	6.9	8.8	7.8	5.7
Forest	2.6	2.4	2.4	2.4	2.4	2.4
Rough grazing	7.8	6.0	5.5	5.5	5.5	5.5
Urban	1.5	1.5	1.5	1.5	1.5	1.5

The area of four arable crops (x10³ha), curently and under five different climatic scenarios.

Crop	1987	Scenario (i)	(ii)	(iii)	(iv)	(v)
Silage maize	10	300	40	40	40	170
Grain maize	0	300	1670	1330	1550	1760
Sunflower	0	200	1110	890	1030	1170
Soya	0	0	770	640	700	820

Table 2 shows that there are significant differences between the actual and the predicted current areas. Some land that is suitable for arable crops of livestock feeding significance is currently under permanent pastures and rough grazing. Thus biological and ecological considerations indicate that total cropping areas, including feed crop areas, are capable of expansion, and this expansion is likely to be even greater with the predicted climatic changes over the next half century. Thus the limitations to feed crop production in the UK are likely to be economic, political and sociological, rather than biological, ecological or climatic.

Considering the simplified nature of the rules, the agreement between the actual and predicted areas is good. Comparing the four future scenarios with the one for the present, the main result is that the arable area seems to be insensitive to temperature change but to depend closely on the water regime. This is in accord with experience, since arable areas are often differentiated from non-arable because of rainfall or soil rather than temperature. Clearly the rainfall regime, which is difficult to predict, will play a key role. The effect of rain will depend on its seasonality as well as the total amount, and it is possible to imagine cases where the annual rainfall rises but the summer rains decline. The effects of seasonality of rainfall have not been included in the calculations.

Of particular relevance to ruminant livestock production is the productivity of the grass crop. This crop is unique in that it is cropped continuously throughout the year albeit with major seasonal fluctuations. It is therefore tempting to suggest that higher soil and ambient temperatures would increase the growing season and hence increase the total biomass production throughout the year as a whole.

Figure 1
The effect of growing season length on annual production of a grass sward

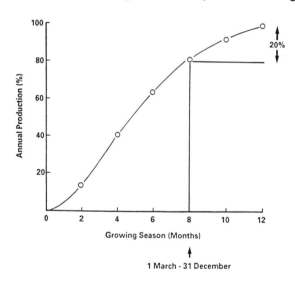

Assumptions

i) Production (t.DM.ha^{-1}) = $\Sigma \int_{t = t_1}^{t = t_2}$ f.Qdt Growing season = $t_2 - t_1$; Q = solar radiation.

ii) Σ, the dry matter radiation quotient, is unaffected by temperature and plant age.

iii) 90% of the incident radiation is absorbed by the canopy (f) except in the first and last month of growth when the proportion falls to 0.50.

iv) the growing season is symmetrical about July 31.

v) Broom Barn (Suffolk) is a representative meterological station.

However, such effects are not likely to be as large as might be expected, because of the limitation set by solar radiation receipts. Figure 1 indicates, from solar radiation data derived from Brooms Barn Experimental Station in Suffolk, the total theoretical annual production of grass according to the length of the growing season. Thus, over a 6-month growing season, about 70% of annual productivity is realised. From 6 to 8 months potential production only increases by 12% and from 8 to 10 months by a further 11%. The actual increase in growing season is likely to be much less than this – of the order of one extra month or so – and thus the increase in total annual grass production is likely to be much less than 10%. Moreover, if the rise in temperature is accompanied by an increase in cloudiness, and thus a reduction in solar radiation, then the beneficial effect of warmer temperatures could easily be cancelled out.

The timing of production is of particular importance in the grass crop where some systems may be limited by the onset of growth of grass in the spring. However, the key date is not actually the date when growth is first observed, but rather the date when the growth rate of the sward is sufficient to allow continued growth even under the pressure of grazing. If it is assumed that a grass sward absorbs 90% of the incident photosynthetically active radiation, that the dry matter: radiation quotient is 3 g/MJ (Russell et al, 1989), and that 10% of the production is partitioned to the roots, then the initial potential growth rate can be computed for swards starting growth at different times of year. A grass sward starting growth in mid-January could grow at a rate of 3 g/m^2/day, whereas one starting growth in mid-April would grow at 16 g/m^2/day. These are over-estimates since initial growth is likely to be depressed by low temperatures, shortage of nitrogen and incomplete leaf canopy. In addition, when conditions are unfavourable for photosynthesis, assimilate is translocated preferentially to the roots and stem base reserves, to the detriment of foliage growth (Gillet et al, 1984). Only foliage growth is relevant to the ruminant animal.

Extending the length of the growing season into the early spring could also pose managerial problems under certain circumstances. If the winters become warmer and wetter, turn-out of cattle onto heavier soils could be limited, not so much by grass growth as by the danger of poaching. If, however, the winters are both warmer and drier, early turn-out becomes much more feasible.

Another consideration with regard to grass growth is the length of the summer drought period. In the drier areas to the east of the UK, growth is limited by shortage of water in mid-summer. Whether or not this summer drought period will worsen or improve will depend entirely upon how annual precipitation patterns will differ from current mean levels. As already stated, changes in annual rainfall are difficult to predict, but hotter, wetter summers would favour increased grass production compared to hotter, drier summers, just as hotter, drier winters would favour early turn-out of in-wintered cattle.

The value of grass is dependent on its nutritional quality as well as its quantity. Nutritional quality is low in the spring when dry matter percentage is low, and also in the late autumn when crude fibre levels are high. It therefore follows that an extension of the growing season into early spring and late autumn will continue to result in the production of extra grass of lower than average quality at both ends of the season. The quality of mid-seasonal grass will depend upon the growing conditions at that time.

To summarise, the effect of higher temperatures is likely to produce less than 10% extra total grass yield, and this extra grass, produced early and late in the season, will be of relatively lower nutritional quality.

DIRECT EFFECTS OF AN INCREASE IN CLIMATIC TEMPERATURE ON LIVESTOCK

An animal responds to the temperature of its environment, which is a consequence of the climatic temperature and the amount by which this is modified by the shelter or housing provided. An increase in climatic temperature may, or may not, increase the temperature experienced by the animal. Where it does lead to an increase there may, or may not, be an effect on animal performance. The factors affecting whether these effects occur or not may be summarised as below.

The effects of temperature on livestock

In the long-term, heat losses must equal heat production. Over a restricted range of temperature, heat loss can be maintained constant but this range may be very narrow (as in the case of day-old chicks) or very wide (as in the case of long-wool sheep). At temperatures below the lower end of this range, known as the lower critical temperature (LCT), heat loss must increase as temperature falls further. At temperatures above the upper end of this range – the upper critical temperature (UCT) – heat loss is insufficient to prevent the temperature of the animal (TA) from rising.

Within limits between LCT and UCT, the animals are in their so-called 'comfort zone' and within this zone biological efficiency is at its maximum. Above the upper limit of the comfort zone, but below UCT, the appetite of the animal will be reduced and feed conversion efficiency will be lower. Reproductive efficiency, especially of the male, will also be impaired.

If an increase in temperature causes the temperature to be above the UCT, feed intake and performance will both fall, efficiency will decrease markedly and reproductive efficiency will be severely impaired.

The relationship between climatic temperature (T_C) and the temperature that the animal experiences (T_A)

The aim is to keep the T_A above the LCT and lower than the UCT. In housed animals this is done by insulating the structure, having a high stocking rate and by varying the ventilation rate. This strategy can be very successful as shown in the data presented in Figure 2.

Where T_C is such that T_A is less than LCT (as with young chicks and piglets in the UK in winter) heat must be used to bring T_A up to the LCT. Where T_A is greater than UCT then expensive cooling techniques could be used to reduce

Figure 2
Environment evaluation
Regression: Mean inside against outside temperature

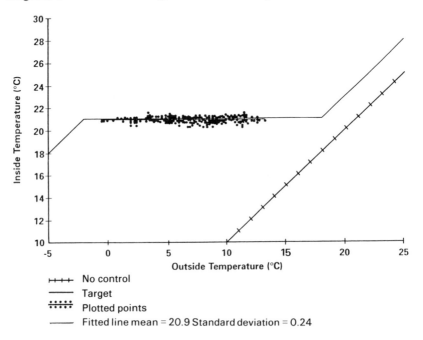

Source: Derived from Charles (1989).

T_A below UCT. The energetic cost of such techniques is very dependent on relative humidity.

In summary, therefore, an increase in the climatic temperature will on the one hand reduce the need for energy in heating pig and poultry houses in the winter, and increase the need to cool such houses in the summer. It is probable that the heating energy saved in winter will exceed the extra energy expended on cooling during the summer and hence an increase of 3°C in mean climatic temperature will tend to increase the overall energetic efficiency of monogastric production.

It would be possible to model all these effects for different classes of livestock against different climatic scenarios, but it is not likely that the refinements thus produced would vary these broad generalisations. Again, the most major differences in energy usage will be between seasons rather than between the past and future mean climatic values.

EFFECT OF LIVESTOCK POPULATION ON GLOBAL METHANE BUDGETS
The current atmospheric concentration of methane is about 1.7 ppmv (Figure 3) and has increased by about 2% per annum on average for the last century. Previous to 1900, methane concentrations were fairly static (see Figure 4).

The ambient temperature would be calculated to increase by about 1°C with a doubling of the current methane concentration, assuming only the direct radiative effects of methane. The atmospheric residence time of methane is about 10 years and is thus very long relative to the reactive trace gases in the atmosphere (ozone residence time is 0.01 year).

Figure 3
Global average tropospheric methane concentration

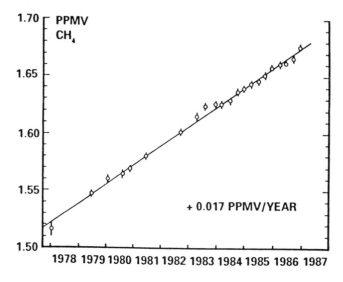

Source: Derived from Blake & Rowland (1987).

Figure 4
Changes in the atmospheric concentration of CH₄ estimated from ice core data

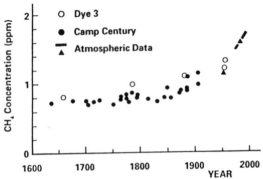

Ice core data are from Craig & Chou (1982) and Rasmussen & Khalil (1984).
Atmospheric data are from Blake & Rowland (1987) and Rinsland et al (1985).

Figure 5
The effect of soil temperature on methane production in fen lands (Minnesota data)

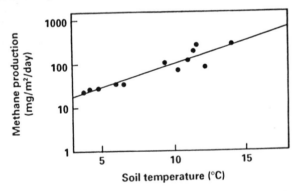

The sources of methane include rice paddies, wetland and tundra. As soil temperature rises so also does the production of methane from these soil types, as shown in Figure 5.

The total input of methane to the atmosphere lies in the range of 300–550 Mt per year. The methane is derived from seven main sources as shown in Figure 6.

It will be seen from Figure 6 that the two dominant sources of methane production are the anaerobic fermentation of organic matter by bacteria in rice paddies, wetlands and tundra, as already discussed. Methane production from the digestive tracts of animals ranks in third place, and

Figure 6
Global emissions of methane (Mt/year)

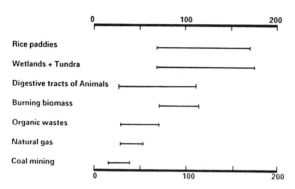

results in a flux to the atmosphere of about 85 Mt per year. This contribution to atmospheric methane has been re-calculated from first principles, using the knowledge that methane output varies markedly between species, is linked to the energy maintenance requirement (expressed as ME) and also to the body size.

Assuming that energy required for animal maintenance is 0.4 MJ of ME/$kg^{0.75}$ per day, then the various methane production rates of different classes of farm animal can be tabulated as shown in Table 3. The data are provided on a global basis since the effect of methane production on climate is not localised.

Table 3
Methane production by livestock

Livestock Class	CH$_4$ production (as % of ME)	Mean wt (kg)	1987 World population (M)
Cattle + Buffalo	8	400	1420
Sheep + Goats	8	40	1660
Camels	6	500	19
Horses	3	450	66
Other equines	3	275	56
Pigs	1.5	60	840

Using this data, the daily methane production of the World's livestock population is equivalent to approximately 6×10^9 MJ of ME per day, of which about three-quarters is derived from cattle and buffalo. By contrast, the methane production by the World's human population (some 5 billion) is approximately 0.4×10^9 MJ of methane per day.

Expressed another way, the total gross energy equivalence of the methane gas produced by the World's livestock population approximates to about 116 Mt of barley per year or 66 Mt of coal a year, or 146 Mt of wood per year (using energy equivalence of 33.5 MJ of GE/kg for coal and 15 MJ of GE/kg for wood).

OTHER LIVESTOCK CONSIDERATIONS
As stated in the introduction, this section will mainly pose questions and suggest possible answers. Key issues are dealt with for which no definitive data are available and consequently the comments made are subjective.

Possible change in the UK livestock population
Climatic considerations are unlikely to be the main factor causing changes in the UK livestock population. Socio-economic and politico-economic considerations are likely to be of much greater importance. Thus, the effect of 1992 on lowering the trading barriers within the EC and the construction of the Channel Tunnel, are more likely to affect the pattern of home production versus importation of livestock products rather than a mere 3°C shift in mean climatic temperatures. Also, any significant shift towards a more vegetarian style of diet, for purely subjective reasons, is likely to be as important a factor in influencing the UK livestock population as a shift towards slightly longer summers and shorter winters.

Possible effect of climatic change on livestock productivity
As has been indicated in an earlier section, livestock have relatively wide 'comfort zones', and providing monogastric animals are warmed in winter and cooled in hot summers there is no reason to believe that the average livestock performance, in terms of biological energetic efficiency, will alter as a result of a 3°C change in mean ambient temperatures. Indeed, changes due to improvements in biological efficiency through breeding, particularly in view of the dramatic improvements likely to occur as a result of new developments in biotechnology, are likely to be of much greater importance in increasing livestock productivity.

Effects of climate on livestock diseases
There are likely to be some effects of climate on both endo- and ecto-parasites but, once again, seasonal differences in climate, and between-year variation in climate, are likely to be as significant as the longer-term cumulative effects of climatic change. It is likely that warmer summers wil

favour certain ecto-parasites, especially ticks. An increase in the number of tick species as well as in the total tick population, could result in the UK being subjected to certain tick-borne diseases currently regarded as 'exotic'.

Bacterial and viral infections of farm animals are also influenced by environmental conditions, but the differences between, for instance, housed cattle and out-wintered cattle and housed sheep and out-wintered sheep are likely to have a greater effect on disease prevalence then a small shift in mean ambient temperature.

Finally, any relaxation of the currently strict quarantine arrangements for animal importations into the UK is likely to have a very much greater effect on the future disease pattern of the UK livestock population than any relatively small change in climatic conditions.

In short, there will be changes in the range and type of diseases affecting farm livestock, but many of these changes are likely to occur as a result of modifying factors entirely distinct from climatic change as such.

CONCLUSION
On balance, a rise of 3°C in mean climatic temperature will be favourable to livestock production both directly, in terms of less energy inputs, and indirectly, in terms of better range and yield of feed and fodder crops.

However, agriculture, as an industry, is a contributor to the global warming process. The livestock population increases global warming through increasing atmospheric methane, and the livestock support industries contribute in a manner similar to non-agricultural industries.

ACKNOWLEDGEMENTS
The author gratefully acknowledges the help given in the preparation of this paper by Drs G Emmans, D Fowler, J D Oldham, J Moncrieff and G Russell.

REFERENCES
Blackman, G E et al(1963) The atlas of Britain and Northern Ireland. Oxford: Clarendon Press.

Central Statistical Office (1988) Monthly digest of statistics No 504.

Eurostat (1988) Agricultural Statistics Yearbook. Theme 5 Series A. Brussels: Eurostat.

Francis, P E (1981) The Climate of the agricultural areas of Scotland. Climatological memorandum No 108. Bracknell: Meteorological Office.

Gillet, M, Lemaire, G & Gosse, G (1984) Essai d'elaboration d'un schema global de la croissance des graminees fourrageres. Agronomie, 4, 75–82.

Russell, G, Jarvis, P J & Monteith, J L (1989) Absorption of radiation by canopies and stand growth. In: Russell, G, Marshall, B & Jarvis, P G (Eds) *Plant Canopies: their Growth, Form and Function*. Cambridge: CUP.

Smith, L P (1984) *The agricultural climate of England and Wales*. MAFF/ADAS Technical Bulletin 35. London: HMSO.

Taylor, J A (1976) Upland climates In: Chandler, T J & Gregory, S (Eds) *The Climate of the British Isles*. London: Longman.

Bennett, R M (Ed) (1989) *The 'greenhouse effect' and UK agriculture*. CAS Paper 19. Reading: Centre for Agricultural Strategy.

5 The implications of the 'greenhouse effect' for fertilizers and agrochemicals

Ken Treharne

INTRODUCTION

From time immemorial, farming, all over the World, has always had to contend with vagaries of weather, political systems and socio-economic pressures. In their main purpose of producing food or raw materials for building, textiles, energy and other industrial processes, farmers continually live in a 'climate of change', but now face a potentially new major challenge of a change in climate through the so-termed 'greenhouse effect'.

Given the doubling of the atmospheric concentration of carbon dioxide during the next 50 years, compared with that quoted for the middle of the 19th century at about 280 ppmv, as well as similar increases in methane and nitrogen oxides that comprise the heat-trapping 'greenhouse' gases, a global increase in temperature of $4°C \pm 1.5°C$ is predicted. These parameters alone have significant implications for 'uncontrolled' natural vegetation of different global regions as well as for agriculture. But of even greater concern is the likely change in climatic systems related to wind patterns and resultant rainfall regimes which, as yet, cannot accurately be predicted on a regional scale, and notably are more complex for the UK through its latitude and maritime/land boundaries. The need for better forecasts of potential change in rainfall scenarios, both in amount and seasonal distribution, is of overriding importance, since these factors will influence land use for cropping systems and management practices more significantly than temperature or CO_2, either alone or as interactive factors.

Professor Harold Woolhouse has already dealt with aspects of crop production, both climatic effects on growth and productivity of current UK major crops, together with the potential for new crop species presently marginal in most years in relation to prevailing UK temperatures.

Measures required for adequate crop nutrition within systems of land use by selected manurial (organic or inorganic) regimes, and those necessary for crop protection of existing or novel crops, either through chemical or biological control need to be considered.

CONSUMER AND POLICY ISSUES

Before embarking on some 'what if' climatic scenarios, perhaps some perspective of practices currently employed in our intensive agricultural systems and of public perception of them is first necessary.

The major questions of public and consumer concern over the perceived, or real, impact of modern North European agriculture on the countryside, the environment and on the safety both of our food and water supplies are applying pressures politically, socially and economically on the farmer, that perhaps outweigh the longer time-frame of concern over the greenhouse effect.

Will the current debate on 'permitted' concentrations of nitrate in potable water supplies be decided on a basis of scientific evidence or on emotive arguments? Will additional concerns over the effects of pesticide use on the ecology of natural flora and fauna, and on food and water residues, lead to the introduction of extreme preventative measures that may threaten the security of the home-grown supply of European food? Can the provision of nourishment of a world population, set to increase from 5 to 6 billion by the early years of the next century, be achieved without chemical intervention to control weeds, pests and diseases?

Extensification of agriculture in western countries and further development of non-chemical 'organic' systems is possible to some extent, although yield penalties and lack of consistency of production of our major arable crops are inevitable. Product quality and shelf life must be questionable and the consumer would have to accept considerably elevated prices. Moreover, more land would need to be brought into production if the UK and Europe were not to return to dependence upon imported staple commodities. This might be both strategically and economically unacceptable, especially if the potential greenhouse effect significantly constrains production of cereal grains, for example in mid-continental North America, which climatic models suggest may be significantly drier and unable to support major production.

AGROCHEMICALS AND TECHNOLOGY

Agrochemicals have helped transform a world in which food shortages and large-scale starvation were a stark reality, and without the judicious use of pesticides the necessary increase by 75% in the World's food supply by the year 2000 (Blaxter, 1986) cannot be achieved. How does a 'developed' western world, concerned with dieting through food excesses, come to terms with the desperate food needs of two-thirds of the World's population?

The advent and rapid development in plant biotechnology has considerable potential to improve the abilty of our main world crops to be more efficient in nutrient use requirements, to show greater durability of resistance to damage by pathogens and pests, and better competition with weed species. But can genetically-engineered resistance to the major pests and diseases be incorporated into major crop varieties in timely ways to cope with the rate of change in pathogen and pest populations? In parallel, studies of predator-prey relationships and biological control provide alternative or integrated measures for dealing with pests and diseases. Several successful strategies in glasshouse and in field crops in certain parts of the World could become more feasible if the UK climate were in future less variable.

CROP GROWTH AND FERTILIZER REQUIREMENTS

The scope of this article does not allow the complexity of crop nutrition and fertilizer requirements in relation to the 'greenhouse effect' predictions to be fully explored. Nitrogen occupies the central position as the key component of the amino acids, proteins and other constituents essential for plant growth, and is the major fertilizer required to drive crop growth and yield. Soil contains large amounts of organic nitrogen which is available to support crop growth only when converted to ammonium and nitrate ions by gradual microbial breakdown.

The major increase in arable yields in the last 30 years is attributable to new varieties, able to take up applied fertilizer nitrogen with an almost linear yield response, given that other nutrients and water are non-limiting and that effective crop protection is achieved. At the same time, soil nitrate that is not taken up by a crop is water soluble and can be washed out by excess rainfall and thus find its way into potable supplies. Current EC Directives suggest a compulsory reduction of nitrates in drinking water to a concentration of 50 mg/l in the belief, unsubstantiated by scientific evidence, that greater concentrations are harmful to health. Were this to be enforced, present arable agriculture and horticultural production systems, particularly in water catchment areas of the UK and northern Europe, will incur severe penalties of yield and profitability. The issues are complex in that major sources of leached nitrates are not directly attributable to fertilizer, but to the mineralisation processes of organic matter in the soil and, of course, to badly-timed applications of manure or chemical fertilizer. Good agricultural practices of early autumn cropping with no applied fertilizer and no bare soil in winter, intermittent use of animal manure and avoidance of ploughing grassland, can help reduce nitrate leaching and the farming industry is applying these principles. The fact remains that arable farming inevitably has to result in some nitrate loss when rainfall exceeds evaporation. Establishment of protection zones to achieve 50 mg/l of nitrate could reduce UK arable agriculture by about 50%. Reduction in fertilizer inputs by 30% would, on average, reduce yield by 22% and only after many years reduce leaching by less than 20%. Long-term manurial experiments at Rothamsted have shown that such leakage took 40 years to decline to half the initial value.

If current dogmas are applied they will have more far-reaching and more immediate impact than a perceived climate change on arable farming in the UK.

THE GREENHOUSE EFFECT AND CROP NUTRITION

Three main issues of crop nutrition can be addressed. Taking a specific 'what if' scenario of a 4°C rise in temperature, double CO2 concentration and a view that our 'island' rainfall may be 40% greater during the winter months (September-February) and 40% smaller during the March-August period, consequences can be estimated for:

    (i)   wheat growth and nitrogen requirement;
    (ii) activity of soil microbes in mineralisation and denitrification and
    (iii) leaching profiles of unused soil nitrates.

Dr John Porter (AFRC Institute of Arable Crops Research, Long Ashton, personal communication) examined the interactive effects of increased temperature and CO_2 and changed rainfall distribution, using a new model for wheat growth and development (AFRCWHT2), which was derived from amalgamating the original AFRCWHT1 with Dr Tom Addiscott's (Institute of Arable Crops Research, Rothamsted) model of nitrate movement through soils (SLIM).

A comparison of the computer simulation of the present and this 'greenhouse-effect' scenario for Avalon wheat grown at Rothamsted in 1985 revealed several important features (see Figure 1).

The enhanced CO_2 and increased temperature provide earlier canopy development and a greater rate of leaf senescence but the higher temperature significantly shortens the period of grain development, losing the advantage of increased dry matter availability. Incorporating the changed rainfall pattern showed little effect on total dry matter production, but grain yield fell to 7.1 t/ha (Harvest Index dropping from 0.48 to 0.34). Assuming the same nitrogen inputs, total plant uptake was lower under 'greenhouse' conditions, whilst unused nitrate capable of being leached increased by a factor of almost 3 (see Figure 1). The simulation of nitrogen input assumed equal rates of soil mineralisation, but microbial breakdown in

Figure 1

A modelled comparison of present-day and greenhouse climate[1] effects on wheat growth and nitrogen uptake and drainage

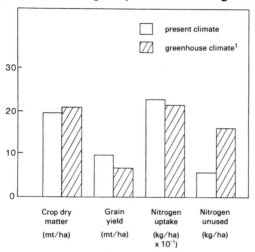

1 (+4°C , × 2 CO_2, 40% wetter winter, 40% drier summer)

Source: Dr J R Porter, personal communication.

the warmer, wetter 'winter' period is likely to be considerably greater and excess rainfall would exacerbate leaching (Addiscott, 1983). Furthermore, no allowance for change in denitrification activity was made (conversion of nitrate to nitrogen oxide), although the process is temperature sensitive (Powlson *et al*, 1988).

These factors clearly require more detailed research, since the patterns and balance of natural 'nitrate turnover' have major implications for crop management and precision of manurial treatments, both in terms of input variable costs and environmental protection. The changed weather patterns, if the wetter winter prediction is generally correct, will also strongly influence farming operations involving vehicular access. There may be scope initially to reduce applied fertilizer inputs, more specifically geared to crop needs and husbandry practice.

Such simulations of CO_2 and temperature are largely based on plant responses determined in controlled environment experiments, which do not adequately reflect field conditions. Nor have experiments been conducted with crops exposed to higher CO_2 and temperature throughout the life cycle. Such studies are needed to validate current models and target physiological attributes for plant breeding, either conventionally or through biotechnology.

CROPPING PATTERNS

If, as predicted, the climate changes result in a drier south-eastern region of the UK, this might constrain current crops in the absence of irrigation. The range of many crop species would move northward, which could involve bringing new land, currently under grassland, into arable production. Obvious dangers are the long-term release of nitrates in addition to the increased turnover of higher levels of soil organic matter associated with more northerly latitudes, that might add to the burden of atmospheric CO_2. This emphasises research needs in soil microbial ecology and the mechanistic study of the interactions between the soil, micro-organisms and the plant root, to provide a basis for efficient and environmentally-sympathetic land use.

I selected for comment the potential greenhouse effect on the main UK cereal crop and fertilizer issues. The situation, modelled for indeterminate crop species such as potato and sugar beet by Squire & Unsworth (1988), based on Marshall's model from the Scottish Crops Research Institute, presents a very different picture, in that yields would be substantially increased subject to restrictions in growth through increased saturation deficits in the summer months. But the temperature and rainfall scenario chosen for comment could lead to a major change in crop timing, even to autumn planting and early summer harvest. What scope is there to improve cold tolerance in our major root crops to achieve this potential, and can we improve higher temperature and water-deficit tolerance attributes to provide options for perceived new climatic conditions?

Mechanistic study at the molecular level of adaptation to, and recovery from, such 'stresses', toward an understanding of the regulation of intermediary metabolism and physiological plasticity of plant species, should be a high priority and is essential to identification of useful genes if the exciting potential of biotechnology is to be of any value.

CROP PROTECTION

In the post-war years, the urgent demand for food in Europe required a dramatic change from previously rotation-based, largely organic farming systems for the major arable crops. The increase in agricultural production necessary to meet the policy of achieving a self-sufficiency in home-grown food, combined with a rapid and progressive fall in farm labour availability, notably in the UK, led to more mechanisation of farm operations and the introduction of chemical control of weeds, pests and diseases. Research developed herbicides, insecticides and fungicides, capable of overcoming inadequacies of alternative means of control, to enable yield and quality to be obtained. Agrochemical control in major world crops, such as wheat, rice, maize, soya and non-food cash crops is relatively recent. For example, fungicide control in UK cereal crops began only 20 years ago, and was an essential part of an integrated production and crop protection system, enabling better expression of the genetic potential for yield of modern cereal varieties responding to increased fertilizer application.

ENVIRONMENTAL AND HEALTH ISSUES

Many would argue that agrochemical pesticides are over-used as an insurance policy by farmers, and present unacceptable threats to wildlife through the non-selectivity of their toxic action and health hazards due to residues in food or through leaching into the potable water supply (as do nitrates). This public perception of risk is the subject of active debate, but must take into account the advantages of pesticides, at this time, in sustaining food resources, maintaining storage and shelf life, protecting consumers against natural poisons such as mycotoxins, and enabling the maintenance of relatively low food costs (which represent only 20% of expenditure of income in the UK today, compared with over 30% 20 years ago). Pesticides are subject to stringent toxicological and environmental scrutiny by registration authorities operating legislation under the Food and Environment Protection Act of 1986, and maximum residue levels (MRLs) for each compound are set with large safety factors to exposure built in. There is little evidence of a scientific approach being adopted in the EC Drinking Water Directive, which appears to have set arbitrary limits irrespective of potential toxicity.

Having stated a case for pesticides at this time, are there viable alternatives or can these be developed for the future to enable a global reduction in chemical intervention? Does the climate change perceived for the UK through the greenhouse effect provide a better opportunity for effective broad-acre crop biological control or improve potential for developing crop materials inherently resistant to, or subject to minimal damage by, pests, diseases and weeds?

WEEDS AND HERBICIDES

If the models for response to high CO_2 and temperature in the growth and yield potential of determinate crops such as cereals, or of the indeterminate ones such as potato are extrapolated to our current weed species, it may be assumed that weed competition in our major crops will become increasingly severe. Indeed, the physiological plasticity of many weed species and their greater genetic diversity within species compared with modern bred crops may provide them with an even greater competitive advantage and the opportunity to invade new environmental niches. Changes in patterns of growth and seed formation, and in the physiological characteristics of dormancy, may give rise to new problems and require different control strategies. The performance of many herbicides is affected directly by temperature and, in addition, the penetration of active molecules of selective herbicides through leaf surfaces is known to be altered if the target plants are subjected previously to temperature and moisture regimes that modify cuticle thickness or surface waxes (Caseley, 1987; Silcox & Holloway, 1989). Whether through altered metabolism or penetration characteristics, the future efficacy of herbicides to control problem weeds may be questioned.

Considerable research effort has been devoted to quantitatively defining the competition of weed species within the population dynamics of major arable crops, in order to establish the necessity or otherwise for control, and to improve the timing and cost-effective use of herbicides. Whilst clearly providing opportunities for farmers to maintain productivity and quality whilst reducing input costs, the same research addresses the selectivity and sensitivity of control towards lowering the chemical load to protect non-target organisms in the ecosystem by reducing aerial drift and the volatilisation of applied sprays, and addresses the effects of active ingredients and their metabolites in the rhizosphere which could potentially leach into the ground water. It seems ironic that elements of this research underpinning public good and environmental issues, are overruled by considerations of 'near-market' benefits to the farming industry and are subject to reduced funding.

PESTS AND DISEASES – PESTICIDE USE

Pest behaviour and the success of pathogen invasion leading to disease development are profoundly affected by rainfall, humidity and temperature. Knowledge of the basic biology of pests and pathogens in relation to these interactive climatic factors, combined with susceptibility of crops to damage at different growth stages, forms the basis of forecasting systems and decision-making for economic control measures. Prediction of potential epidemics based on weather history and crop monitoring, for which more sensitive and rapid diagnostic aids are becoming available, is still bedevilled by the inaccuracy of weather forecasting on a regional or more local scale. The current major aphid and virus problem in the UK, resulting from an unexpectedly mild winter, serves to emphasise this point.

The 'greenhouse' climate would have significant consequences both to the prevalence and severity of diseases and pest attacks on our major crops. Because of the uncertainty surrounding the magnitude or rate of climatic change, notably in moisture status and dew that relies on net thermal radiation at night, it is very difficult to forecast change in pest and disease problems or what measures will be needed for economic control. These same factors cast doubt on the consistency and sustainability of biological control methods. Much depends on what changes might occur in crops, their regional distribution, and in cultural practices, notably a change in calendar timing such as spring crops planted in the autumn. These would, however, not be new to British agriculture, since in the past 20 years oilseed rape has become a new major crop and the majority of wheat and barley crops are now autumn- rather than spring-sown. These changes brought a new spectrum of problems with pests and diseases, which are successfully controlled by pesticides.

Milder and wetter winters will affect the diversity of pests and beneficial insects affecting agriculture. Aphids are among the most important group of pests, feeding directly on the plant's phloem. They transmit many important plant virus diseases. Their life cycle is complex, having both sexual and asexual phases. Sexual reproduction is induced by declining day length but mediated by temperature. A proportion of the population reproduces asexually on crop hosts throughout the year, and so aphids survive and reproduce more successfully in warmer winters. At any stage in the life cycle, winged forms migrate between different host or crop plants.

The Rothamsted Insect Survey suction trap network throughout the UK has, for over 25 years, monitored aphid abundance, phenology and the proportion carrying virus. In spring, the number of anholocyclic migrants is determined by winter temperature and earlier infestation. Virus transmission from holocyclic clones creates the greatest damage to crops. Thus in a greenhouse climate, the warmer winter of Scotland would no longer protect the seed potato industry from virus attack; early infection of sugar beet would greatly increase damage by virus yellows, and current 'safe windows' for planting to avoid cereal viruses would disappear. Indeed, the situation of higher temperature and CO_2 could change crop physiology and host status such that more generations of aphids per year are likely. Changes in individual species and the impacts of natural enemies of aphids are also possible, and such relative changes in predator-prey relationships might offer eventual opportunities for biological control. Research at Rothamsted into antifeedant properties of natural plant 'semiochemicals', seeks to understand the regulation of their biochemical pathways with a view to transferring controlling genes to crop species. Together with insect-disturbing pheromones, such an approach may ultimately lead to the ability to reduce aphicide applications, and there is much scope to develop more selective and less environmentally harmful insecticides for the future.

If the greenhouse climate encouraged a new range of crops such as maize, sunflower and soybean, there would inevitably be new pest problems; leaf beetles, Colorado beetle, cutworms and other Lepidopterous pests are likely to increase in arable and forestry crops. Honey-bees but not bumble-bees are likely to flourish in a warmer climate. As with insects, different crops would introduce a new spectrum of nematodes, including several migratory species. Milder winters and warmer summers would provide conditions for survival of several species of root-knot nematodes, currently of concern only in glasshouse crops. Other soil pests such as slugs, already major problems, would thrive in warmer moisture conditions, and whilst there may be opportunities for biological control through harnessing fungal pathogens involved in nematode decline in natural conditions, sustainability of control is uncertain. Plant applied and downward (phloem) mobile pesticides would provide an opportunity for better targetted chemical control, but there is a need for a better understanding of plant transport mechanisms and the biology of pests to provide more 'bio-rational' approaches.

In speculating on changes in pests and diseases, parallels have been drawn from regions that currently have climates postulated for the future in the UK. With hotter and drier summers (as say in Morocco) or a climate more akin to central and southern Europe, the relative dominance of pathogen species is likely to change. Thus the *Septoria* diseases of wheat would shift from a dominance of *S. tritici* in the UK to *S. nodorum*, related mainly to temperature effects (see Figure 2).

But if rainfall decreases, these and other splash-dispersed pathogens, such as *Rhynchosporium* and eyespot, may decrease in importance, whilst the wind-dispersed pathogens would be less affected. Were cropping patterns to change to autumn-sown, shorter-season, rainfed crops over 'winter' and irrigated, high-value crops in summer, notably in the south-eastern UK, current diseases would be equally problematic and yellow rust on wheat and the splash-borne pathogens may be worse. Fungal and bacterial pathogens may quickly become a problem on new crops, since they

Figure 2
Temperature responses of *Septoria* diseases of wheat

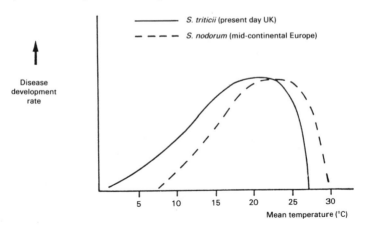

Source: D Royle, personal communication.

are able to take advantages of new ecological niches. More luxurious weed growth is likely to provide new major reservoirs as primary or secondary hosts of disease-causing organisms, and the relative importance of vector-transmitted viruses will change. Black stem rust and leaf rusts could become an increasing threat and *Fusarium* infections both of root (footrots) and ears (plus mycotoxin production) are likely to become more serious. If seasonality of production is unchanged, root infection by 'take-all' may increase in severity, notably if crops are subject to water deficits. For the root crops, *Cercospora* and downy mildew of sugar beet, the yellows complex of viruses and *Rhizomania* will grow in importance, favoured by milder winters. Other viruses transmitted by leaf hoppers, whiteflies and mites are almost certain to cause problems.

For many of these pests and diseases there are inadequate data on their epidemiology related to interactions of temperature and moisture status, and on the susceptibility of plants to invasion and tissue response. Present knowledge of yield loss assessments and pesticide spray thresholds will be inadequate, and we cannot extrapolate current models of disease control or efficacy of pesticides with any certainty. In the medium- and probably the longer-term, fungicide and insecticide use will continue to be required to cope with the interacting new spectra of pests and diseases attacking crops, either simultaneously or at different times in the growth cycle. Continued research on sensitive targetted application with minimal harm to the environment is thus critical and, in parallel, effort should be intensified on providing understanding of mechanisms of genetic resistance at the molecular level. The question of how to harness genes conferring resistance or tolerance to the diverse army of pests and diseases into our present or future major crops, whilst maintaining the important agronomic attributes of yield and quality, will take some time to answer.

CONCLUSION

In summary, if release of CO_2 and other 'greenhouse' gases in the World continues and global warming ensues, major changes will occur in UK agriculture in crop growth, species and regional distribution. Nutritional requirements will need carefully to be re-evaluated, and dramatic changes in weed, pest and disease problems will require to be controlled if food supply and quality is to be sustained.

Although biological research is making exciting discoveries at a rapid pace, there seems little choice, in view of the scale and complexity of weeds, pests and diseases on a world-scale, of protecting food crops adequately in the foreseeable future other than by agrochemicals. Safer and more environmentally acceptable chemicals and agricultural practices are needed if the consumer is to be convinced.

ACKNOWLEDGEMENT
I have drawn freely on the thoughts of my senior colleagues in the AFRC Institute of Arable Crops, Professor T Lewis, Dr T Addiscott, Dr K J Brent, Dr B Kerry, Dr J Porter, Dr R Plumb, Dr D Powlson and Dr D Royle, whose help and expertise are much appreciated.

REFERENCES
Addiscott, T M (1983) Kinetics and temperature relationships of mineralisation and nitrification in Rothamsted soils with differing histories. *Journal of Soil Science*, **34**, 343-353.

Blaxter, Sir K (1986) *People, food and resources*. Cambridge University Press.

Caseley, J C (1987) Effects of weather on herbicide activity. In: Lemerle & Leys (Eds) *Proceedings of the 8th Australian Weed Conference 1987*. Sydney: Council of Australian Weed Science Societies, 386-394.

Powlson, D S, Saffigna, P G & Kragt-Cottaar, M (1988) Denitrification at sub-optimal temperatures in soils from different climatic zones. *Soil Biology & Biochemistry*, **20**, **5**, 719-723.

Silcox, D & Holloway, P J (1989) Foliar absorption of some nonionic surfactants from aqueous solutions in the absence and presence of pesticide active ingredients. In: Chow, P *et al* (Eds) *Adjuvants and Agrochemicals 1. Mode of Action and Physiological Activity*. Bocco Ratan: CRC Press, 115-128.

Squire, G R & Unsworth, M H (1988) *Effects of CO_2 and climatic change on agriculture*. Report to the Department of the Environment.

Bennett, R M (Ed) (1989) *The 'greenhouse effect' and UK agriculture*. CAS Paper 19. Reading: Centre for Agricultural Strategy.

6 Economic dimensions of the 'greenhouse effect' for UK agriculture

John Marsh

THE GREENHOUSE EFFECT – A STARTING POINT

The extent of global warming, or indeed whether it will occur at all, has been a matter of dispute among experts. In general the impression given to the layman, including the economist, is of a process which extends well into the next century. In the United Kingdom this is expected to result by the middle of the next century in a rise of some 3°C in average temperature (Wright & Hill, 1989). The Department of Environment Report (DOE, 1988) used a similar prediction as the basis for their desk reviews. This increase will not take place uniformly across Britain. Global sea levels are expected to rise due to the expansion of water as it warms. Predictions range from 15 cm (Farmer & Warrick, 1989) to 200 cm (Revkin, 1988). The DOE report uses a rise of 80 cm for UK sea levels as the 'most likely' prediction. The fact remains that even a small rise in sea level would require substantial investment in coastal fortification. It cannot be assumed, for example, that the relative temperatures of north and south will remain similar. Indeed one of the more alarming notions is that the Gulf Stream might alter its course. If so, the UK would presumably become colder in a warmer world (Mintzer, 1988).

The issue is, of course, not simply a matter of temperature. Rainfall, the seasonal distribution of rain, the days which are frost free and the extent of the peaks of heat, will all condition what sorts of agriculture can be continued and what will be the costs of production. It is too simple to extrapolate from the situation in more southern regions of Europe in order to guess what might occur in Britain. In contrast, it is clear that some of the land lost as a result of a rise in sea levels would be very high quality lowland. The impact on production might thus be disproportionately large.

CONTEMPORARY PRESSURES ON AGRICULTURAL POLICY

In exploring the economic implications of this predicted change in climate it is essential to place it within the context of other developments which will also affect agriculture during this period. A number of these can be identified.

(i) The industry is facing a substantial reduction in investment in response to current problems of market imbalance. This may reduce not only productive capacity in the immediate future but also research and innovation during the next decade. Such cuts in resources and ideas will reduce the number of strategies open to farmers if significant climatic changes occur.

(ii) The UK industry has to compete within the EC and the EC has to compete within the World. In both areas significant changes will occur in the period during which the greenhouse effect becomes apparent. The EC seems likely to constrain farm production in ways which protect the small family farm. Such a policy is inconsistent with the most efficient use of resources, measured in terms of market signals. It also is likely to discriminate against the UK, where farms are generally larger than in other member countries. An industry whose resources are trapped in obsolete patterns would face additional difficulty in seeking to cope with changes, whether from the climate or from the market. Globally it will be able to command a smaller market share. Nationally it will provide fewer people with satisfactory incomes.

(iii) Current negotiations in the GATT have had to include agriculture in order for any satisfactory resolution to be achieved. It is still far from clear what this will mean for the EC. However, some limits on the EC's ability to fix prices and subsidise exports, together with some increased access to the EC market for third countries seems inevitable. That will add to the industry's problems, increasing either the amount of structural change required or demanding yet larger visible transfers from other sectors to preserve traditional agriculture.

(iv) The perception of what the public wants from agriculture is changing in most developed countries. Two decades ago, the need was primarily to ensure an adequate volume of food. Today the requirement is more complex. Agriculture has to provide, in addition to a secure and nutritious food supply, a pleasant landscape with plenty of suitable habitats for a varied wildlife. Modern farming methods are believed to threaten this.

Constraints in the response of the industry are also imposed by some attitudes to recent developments – novel techniques used in the food industry are looked at with alarm. Resistance to irradiated foodstuffs, the movements towards 'organic farming' and 'additive free' foods reflect such concerns. The industry and Government have not managed to reassure the public that the food they buy is safe. For example, the 'E' number system, designed to make explicit what additives have been included in manufactured food and taken from a set carefully screened to avoid risks to health, is actually seen by many consumers as indicating the use of unnatural and unhealthy ingredients.

Concern about the methods farmers use to breed and rear animals is not confined to a lunatic fringe which invade laboratories and destroy the work of scientists. Larger-scale farming, the removal of hedges and the extent of 'mono-culture' of cereals, is thought to damage both the appearance of the landscape and the rural communities which remain there.

Increasingly such 'green' issues have come to dominate agricultural policy debates. Agriculture and the food industry will have to cope with the greenhouse effect with a technology which is acceptable. Its past record of response to changes in the economic environment cannot therefore be assumed to be a good predictor of how it may adapt in the future.

THE ECONOMIC DEBATE
The economist's contribution
Economists are concerned with the use of resources. They attempt to analyse the ways in which changing events will alter their distribution and to assess how far the pattern which emerges represents an optimum means of providing what the community wants. In this context, the greenhouse effect is just one of a number of changing events which will influence resource use. Among these changing events are many which will affect resource use in agriculture that stem from market pressures. Central to these are assumptions about the level and distribution of income, the progress of new technology in the production and distribution of food and the implications of shifts in the supply and demand for some raw materials which agriculture uses or for which it might provide substitutes. Government activities will influence the extent of this market and the efficiency with which market signals are transmitted to producers. World agriculture is fragmented by protectionist policies. If this continues opportunities to use resources more efficiently in a new climatic situation may be frustrated by agricultural policies.

There are however many important goods and services which we acquire as a society rather than buy as individuals. These include many intangibles which are significant for agriculture, such as the landscape and the existence of an attractive pattern of wildlife. In these areas society employs, and the economist must observe, political processes to identify priorities. Some environmental threats and opportunities which might flow from the greenhouse effect fall into this category.

The economic implications of the greenhouse effect thus require an analysis both of the ways in which markets may be affected and the response of the political process. This paper discusses both.

THE SUPPLY OF FARM PRODUCTS AND THE PRODUCTION IMPLICATIONS OF THE GREENHOUSE EFFECT

Markets shift resources by altering the incentives offered to those who control them. If, for the moment, we assumed that the prices offered to farmers were unchanged then we can discuss the impact of the greenhouse effect in terms of its consequences for farmers' costs and the amount they would produce. Two hypothetical examples illustrate the possibilities.

First, let it be assumed that the climatic change is to a climate more beneficial for frost sensitive plants. Rainfall is assumed to adjust so that plants are not normally stressed for lack of water (see Friends of the Earth, 1988, which considers increases in rainfall over much of Western Europe in most seasons, although there may be a decrease in spring rainfall in the UK). The growing season would be longer.

The rise in temperature would mean that determinate crops, such as cereals, ripened more quickly. Their yield would be lower although their quality might be improved. For some farms, under suitable conditions, it might be possible to achieve more than one crop product in a single season. If so, the total volume of harvestable material would be increased. The DOE Report (DOE, 1988) recognises that species at their northern limits will be capable of expanding northwards. Under the same favourable assumptions, grass, an indeterminate crop, would grow throughout the year. Given the greater supply of grazing, milk, beef and sheep production potential would be increased. The production possibilities of this model would move towards what we now associate with New Zealand.

The aggregate production potential would be diminished by any loss of land to the sea. However, losses on the scale thought probable by most scientific opinion suggest that the net impact on food production potential of the greenhouse effect seems likely to be positive.

These attractive consequences would be accompanied by a number of extra problems. Diseases which at present are limited by winter frosts would become more prevalent. Some types of pest would multiply (a view supported by Wright & Hill, 1989). The longer growing season would make heavier demands on labour, capital and management. Overall, however, one suspects that most farmers would welcome the new environment. Their costs would tend to fall. The output of agriculture, under our assumption of unchanged prices, would rise. In aggregate, farm incomes would be increased. The benefits might be most marked in those regions currently subject to severe winters.

In contrast, assume that the temperature rise associated with the greenhouse effect is accompanied by an increased problem of water shortage. This seems quite plausible and is recognised as such in the DOE Report. At higher temperatures more rain would be needed to meet the needs of plants. The effects would be complex but potentially are alarming. Husbandry practices would need to adapt to avoid increased erosion, especially in some of the most productive agricultural regions. Plant varieties would need to be used which could grow and be harvested when water was available. Irrigation would play a much larger part in farming. Those places where a reliable supply of irrigation water existed might become very productive, a sort of 'North Atlantic California'. For example, in the south of the EC, if rainfall was particularly low, agricultural practice would need to be modified to avoid any risk that deserts might develop. Farming could become very extensive if it existed at all.

The aggregate impact of such a scenario is difficult to assess, even with the unrealistic aid of unchanged prices. Output of much traditional agriculture would fall. Milk, potatoes, sugar beet, grass-based livestock enterprises and many of our contemporary cereal types would diminish in supply. However, some new products might appear. Sorghum, soybeans, tobacco and subtropical fruits and vegetables might thrive in favoured places. In addition, it seems possible that prices would rise, attracting into farming additional resources to combat the lack of water. More alarmingly, some regions, notably the hills and mountains, would become difficult to exploit and suffer a high risk of erosion. The agriculture of the Appenines may provide some guide as to the sort of activities which could survive in the hill regions of the UK, assuming a climate of this type.

This extremely schematic and simplified exploration of the impact on supply of two contrasting, but not implausible, types of assumption about the greenhouse effect demonstrates that significant implications for British agriculture are possible. It justifies the current concern to study and evaluate the predictions and dimensions of climatic change more carefully.

AGRICULTURE AND FOOD DEMAND RESPONSES TO THE GREENHOUSE EFFECT

The economic implications of a changed supply potential will depend upon what happens to demand. We can now explore some of the factors which will influence demand, consumer response to changed supply conditions, changes in consumption patterns which might result from the greenhouse effect itself, and changes in the level of real incomes.

Within the UK, consumers have access to supplies from all over the World. The controls associated with the Common Agricultural Policy mean that third country products are only available at prices which do not undercut those fixed by the Council of Ministers. If we assume that this political structure remained unchanged, then the amount of British farm output which is bought will be determined first by the impact of the greenhouse effect on EC production and secondarily by its impact worldwide.

Within the Community it seems likely that the southern regions may suffer from inadequate precipitation. This would restrict their agriculture and make it less competitive with that of more northerly regions. Population in the Community as a whole is relatively static, increasing by only 3% in the period between 1976-1986 (calculated from CEC, 1988). Thus demand Community-wide seems likely to depend on income growth. Here there are some positive features. The long-run economic impact of the single market from 1992 should raise real incomes.

'Overall it would seem possible to enhance the Community's annual potential growth rate, for both output and consumption, by around 1 percentage point for the period up to 1992. In addition, there would be good prospects that longer-run dynamic effects could sustain a buoyant growth rate farther into the 1990's.' (Emerson et al, 1988).

Although estimates of such a complex development as completion of the internal market can only be regarded as approximate, the authors quoted make the following judgements about the timing and scale of such changes in income. The major impacts would become apparent after a medium-run time lapse of 5 to 6 years. The cumulative effect in terms of GDP would be between +4.5% and +7%, depending on the development of macroeconomic policy (passive or active).

After the recession of the early 1980s, the European economies have recovered, and whilst further cyclical disturbances are probable, it is clearly premature, leaving aside the '1992 factor', to believe that Europe has 'run out of growth'. Despite this, the growth in effective demand for agricultural raw materials is likely to be modest. The income elasticity of demand for food products, a measure of the proportionate increase in quantity bought for a given rise in income, is low. In the UK in 1987 the income elasticity calculated for food was 0.10 (MAFF, 1987). As a result, given modest optimism about output in the context of the greenhouse effect, it is improbable that the EC demand will be adequate to sustain EC prices.

The crucial issue then becomes what will happen to demand in world markets. Some important producing and exporting regions seem to be at risk. In other areas new climatic conditions might greatly enhance production. Some estimates suggest that production in the US mid-west, a major source of cereals for the World as well as the US, will be seriously impeded (Benci et al, 1975; Waggoner, 1983; Ramirez et al, 1975). There will be more years of drought, so that the stock required to ensure recoverable stability in world prices will rise. In contrast, a warmer climate, especially if accompanied by greater rainfall, might significantly raise USSR

Table 1
Income and price elasticities of demand for selected food categories

Food product	Income elasticity	Price elasticity
Milk and cream	-0.13	-0.13
Potatoes	-0.43	-0.14
Bread	-0.18	-0.25
Fresh fruit	0.66	-0.53
Fresh green vegetables	0.37	-0.39
Other fresh vegetables	0.35	-0.24

Source: MAFF (1987).

production, possibly to an extent which offsets losses elsewhere (Pitovranov *et al*, 1988; National Defense University, 1983). At this stage no unquestioned view exists – another important reason for research.

However, even if we assume that the net effect on world prices was neutral, some interesting results ensue. In terms of economists' jargon, the products which might be in greater supply from UK farms have different elasticity characteristics than the current bundle of outputs. Table 1 demonstrates that at the level of the household, fruit and vegetables are both more price and income elastic than milk and the basic foods such as bread and potatoes.

As a result, if current real incomes are sustained, extra British output would not depress prices in the UK market so much as an equivalent increase in production of the present mix of products. For those farmers able to exploit such products the greenhouse effect's impact on the pattern of relative prices might represent some relief from the constraints of present production. The DOE Report concurs with the idea of an adjusted product mix.

The response of consumers to changed supply conditions for the various products of farms might well be significantly altered by shifts in consumption resulting from the new, warmer climate. Even within the UK, substantial variations in diet occur between north and south. These suggest that diets might shift towards more fruit and vegetables, more wine and less beer, meat and milk. In such a situation, price and income elasticity data derived from current expenditure could be irrelevant.

Agriculture and food form an important component within a much larger UK economy. The share of total consumer spending on food has fallen, and in 1987 represented only 13% of total consumer expenditure. Spending on alcoholic drink accounted for 6.7% of consumer expenditure. The greenhouse effect and measures to cope with it may thus lead to changes in the level of real income in the UK.

OTHER ECONOMIC CONSIDERATIONS

Some negative non-agricultural aspects are obvious. Measures to protect coastal towns from flooding, or if these are impossible the relocation of their people and industries, would make heavy demands on investment. Such investment would simply protect existing output, not increase it. As a result, economic growth prospects would be impaired. According to assumptions made about rainfall, it seems probable that a warmer climate would require greater investment in the water industry. Some land currently used for farming and other economic activities would be lost. Again, how substantial a loss depends on the extent of the global warming and the extent to which measures taken to protect land succeed.

There are some positive features. Energy costs for heating would be reduced. The cost of some domestic construction requirements would fall. Tourism and the associated leisure industries might be encouraged – not least as a refuge from unpleasantly hot conditions further south in Europe. A reduction in days of frost and snow would reduce maintenance costs of roads and railways, whilst the travel accident rate should be reduced.

Such purely domestic economic shifts are likely to be dwarfed by the impact of the greenhouse effect on the world economy. The UK is dependent on trade to sustain its standard of living. As has already been argued, it is premature to make judgements about the consequences for world agricultural production. *A fortiori*, it is unrealistic to jump to conclusions about the overall economic effect. However, it is improbable that a major change in climate could occur without consequences for global investment and the flow of trade. One key element will be the level of investment in the countries of the Pacific rim. Here, recent growth has been an important dynamic of the world economy. If this is impeded, global income is likely to be lower and the trade opportunities for all trading countries, including Britain, to be reduced.

Many other factors, some much more potent than the greenhouse effect, will be simultaneously influencing the level of real income in the UK and the World. A brief list of these illustrates the range and complexity of relevant issues.

(i)   The success with which some heavily indebted developing countries cope with the need both to service old debts and to continue new investment will remain one important element in determining the rate of global economic growth.

(ii) The energy crisis of the 1970s provides a foretaste of resource shortage problems, which are likely to recur from time to time as global income and population grow.

(iii) Since the Industrial Revolution, the self-conscious application of science to industrial production has made a decisive contribution to raising living standards. Such new technology has become available on an accelerating scale. Currently, the electronic revolution is transforming and enhancing productive potential. New bio-technology offers tantalising prospects of plants and animals better equipped to make more productive use of resources. There is at least a hope, on the timescale of the greenhouse effect, of energy production by nuclear fusion which would transform the real income potential of the world economy.

(iv) Rising real incomes have been associated with growing pollution. The greenhouse effect is itself one example. If the world economy is to sustain real incomes, such pollution problems will need to be confronted and removed. In the short-term this implies added cost. In the long-term it is a condition of survival and an opportunity for some industries to grow.

(v) The most serious threat to real incomes is conflict. The success of the European regions in avoiding war has been a major reason for the rise in real incomes in the second half of this century. Whilst a nuclear catastrophe may be avoided, on the timescale of the greenhouse effect history suggests a significant probability of wars, if not of a global then of a regional character, such as have been experienced in the Far and Middle East in the 1970s and 1980s. These, even if Europe is not directly involved, reduce income and threaten the economic system.

Within this context, the overall effect of global warming on real income may prove a relatively minor element.

THE SHAPE OF BRITISH AGRICULTURE AND THE PRESSURES ON POLICY MAKERS

The consequence of putting together the assumptions made earlier about supply and demand conditions, is that pressure would exist for farmers to shift their resource use towards a pattern of agriculture more like that of farmers further south in Europe. On favourable views of supply conditions and current technology, a larger share of cereal and cereal-based products might be imported but in the grass-based enterprises and in fruit and vegetables the UK might become a much more effective competitor. Should rainfall prove a severe restraint, the country might become rather more dependent on imports for food supply - although not reaching the point at which desert Middle-Eastern Sheikdoms provide a model. How the industry responds will depend upon the prices farmers are offered, and hence upon changes both in world prices and the CAP. As is argued above, we do not have enough information to make sensible comment about the likely trend in world prices, but it is possible to note some pressures which might ensue for the CAP.

As was suggested earlier, if there is a general warming of the climate in the north, combined with adequate rainfall, production overall seems likely to become less costly in these regions. Grazing enterprises, milk, beef and sheep, would become capable of competing more effectively on the world scale and the case for protection would be significantly weakened. Cereal production might be depressed by lower yield, but such an outcome could well be mitigated through continued technical progress. The challenge to the Community policy maker would be similar in kind to that currently experienced, but reinforced in degree. To ensure that a competitive industry emerges, prices must be allowed to fall. To do so will, however, impose severe pressure on some of the EC's poorer farmers, especially those living in the south. To avoid wastage, new, more targeted instruments of policy will be needed and may well be resisted by northern members who will see themselves as 'footing the bill'.

In contrast, more difficult growing conditions, associated with increased problems of water shortage, would tend to relieve the 'surplus' problems of the Community but intensify its 'social' problems. Less cereals and milk would be produced in the north. Pig and poultry production would be affected by higher feed costs. In the south, an extreme shortage of rainfall could impede existing production, making farming more dependent upon irrigation. Lowering prices to compete on a world scale would become politically more difficult. The gap between 'world' and 'EC' prices would remain, excess supplies being limited by quantitative measures such as quotas on sales or 'set aside', rather than price pressures. The problems of rural poverty would encourage governments to divert funds from price support towards structural measures and to the support of many small family farms.

It seems possible that whilst the greenhouse effect might relatively strengthen the production potential of British agriculture within the Community, the impact of policy will be less favourable. Given an optimistic assumption, the UK industry might provide a larger share of EC production but at relatively lower prices, compared to world levels, than those which have prevailed in this decade. If a more pessimistic view is taken, the demands to provide social support for large numbers of relatively poor farmers in the south of the Community are likely to be a continued net drain on the UK economy, whilst affording no relief to UK farmers.

EPILOGUE
This exploration of the impact of the greenhouse effect on British agriculture is inescapably inconclusive. The dimensions of the change in climate are uncertain and its impact on farming simultaneous with other changes in the economy and in the technology available to the industry. Where the climatic and other changes work in the same direction, the implications for farm

output and profitability could be substantial. In such circumstances the greenhouse effect may seem to be the precipitating cause. Where the climatic shift is offset by other adjustments its consequences may be imperceptible.

Such a conclusion, although undramatic, is not an excuse for complacency. At this stage we know too little about the greenhouse effect to be able to make rational adjustments in terms of the timing or scale of its impact. We do have evidence which is disturbing and needs more analysis. Two lessons emerge for the economy. First, it would be wise, on these grounds as well as in terms of the prudent use of non-renewable resources, to pursue with vigour technologies which make more efficient use of energy, particularly of fossil fuels. This at least should extend the period of adjustment. Second, we need to sustain and extend research and development, not only into the greenhouse effect itself, but also into all technologies which enable agriculture to cope with the inevitable uncertainties of operating in a changing natural environment.

REFERENCES

Benci, J F, Runge, E C A, Dale, R F, Duncan, W G, Curry, R B & Schaal, L A (1975) Effects of hypothetical climate change on production and yield of corn. In: US Department of Transportation. Climatic Impacts Assessment Project (CIAP). *Impacts of climatic change on the Biosphere*. Washington, 4.3–4.36.

CEC (1988) *Demographic Statistics*. Luxembourg: CEC. 61.

DOE (1988) *Possible impacts of climate change on the natural environment in the United Kingdom*.

Emerson, M, Aujean, M, Catinat, M, Goybet, P & Jacquemin, A (1988) *The economics of 1992. The EC Commission's assessment of the economic effects of completing the Internal Market*. Oxford University Press, 3–6.

Farmer, G & Warrick, R (1989) Agriculture in a changing environment. *Shell Agriculture*, **3**, 4–7.

Friends of the Earth (1988) *The Heat Trap: The threat posed by rising levels of greenhouse gases*. Briefing paper prepared by Karas, J H W & Kelly, P M. University of East Anglia.

Land and Water (1989) The 'greenhouse effect' and agriculture. *Land and Water*, **January**, 6–7.

MAFF (1987) *Household food consumption and expenditure: 1986*, Section 5, HMSO.

MAFF (1988) *Household food consumption and expenditure: 1987*. HMSO.

Mintzer, I (1988) *Living in a Warmer World: Challenges for Policy Analysis and Management*. Association for Public Policy Analysis.

National Defense University (1983) *World grain economy and climate change to the year 2000: Implications for policy.* Report on the final phase of a climate impact assessment. Research Directorate of the National Defense University. Washington DC: Fort Lesley J. McNair.

Parry, M L, Carter, T & Konijn, N (Eds) (1988) *The impact of climatic variations on agriculture.* Summary of a two-volume work for International Institute for Applied Systems Analysis and the United Nations Environment Program. Kluwer Publications.

Pitovranov, S E, Lakinets, V, Kiselev, V I & Sirotenko, O D (1988) The effects of climatic variations on agriculture in the subarctic zone of the USSR. In: Parry, M L *et al* (Eds) *The impact of climatic variations on agriculture. Vol 1. Assessment in cool temperate and cold regions.* Dordrecht: Reidel Publ. Co.

Ramirez, J, Sakamoto, C & Jensen, R (1975) Agricultural implications of climatic change. In: US Department of Transportation. Climatic Impacts Assessment Project (CIAP). *Impacts of climatic change on the Biosphere.* Washington 4.37-4.90.

Revkin, A C (1988) Endless summer: Living with the greenhouse effect. *Discover*, **October**.

Smit, B, Ludlow, L & Brklacich, M (1988) Implications of global climatic warming for agriculture: A review and appraisal. *Journal of Environmental Quality*, **October–December**. 17; 519-527.

Waggoner, P E (1983) Agriculture and a climate changed by more carbon dioxide. In: National Research Council. *Changing climate. Report of the carbon dioxide committee, Board of Atmospheric Sciences and Climate.* Washington DC: National Academy Press. 383–418.

Wright P & Hill, G (1989) A future of feast or of famine? *The Times*, **Feb 28**, 13.

Bennett, R M (Ed) (1989) *The 'greenhouse effect' and UK agriculture*. CAS Paper 19. Reading: Centre for Agricultural Strategy.

Poster presentation: The best place to study the greenhouse effect is in a greenhouse

M Bradley

INTRODUCTION

It was 60 years ago that scientists at Imperial College and the Research Station at Cheshunt (the forerunner of the Glasshouse Crops Research Institute at Littlehampton) showed that crop yields could be increased by enhancing the CO_2 in the atmosphere. Since the 1960s when cheap sources of CO_2 became available, detailed experimental development work has been carried out by the Agricultural Development and Advisory Service (ADAS) at Experimental Horticulture Stations (EHSs). The fully computerised control facilities in commercial-scale greenhouses enable environments to be accurately controlled. Guidelines and blueprints have been worked out for commercial growers. The optimum amount and method of CO_2 enrichment has been documented for many greenhouse crops such as tomatoes, cucumbers, lettuce, chrysanthemums and so on. The technique has been so successful at increasing yields that the viability of enterprises depends on it for success.

HIGHER YIELDS
Lettuce

By increasing CO_2 levels to 1000 ppmv during daylight hours in winter, plant weight increases can be as high as 40%. This high level of CO_2 can be maintained without difficulty in winter and early spring, when outside temperatures are low, because the ventilators are closed for most of the time.

91

Cucumbers
Even when the ventilators are open in summer, a cucumber crop uses CO_2 at a faster rate than it can be naturally replaced, so that levels are below ambient (350 ppmv). By simply maintaining the CO_2 at 350 ppmv throughout the summer, yields are increased by 10%.

Tomatoes
Yields have been increased by 15% when the CO_2 level has been maintained at 500 ppmv in summer.

HOW WILL ARABLE CROPS RESPOND TO INCREASED CO_2?
Research workers have subjected single or small groups of plants in laboratory situations to increased levels of CO_2. As a result of these experiments, prediction models have been produced for some field crops. However, in order that these models can be tested, much larger-scale trials, where plants are growing in association, are required. This is essential if sensible decisions are to be taken about the future of UK agriculture. ADAS has the facilities at the EHSs to carry out detailed large-scale experiments on arable crops and these would test many aspects of the models. Crops could be subjected to various levels of CO_2 and temperature, with added control over water, pests and diseases during the whole of the plants' life cycle. Experiments in controlled conditions on this scale (up to 0.1 ha per plot), at relatively low cost, would give a much better understanding of how crops would grow and yield, and give a much better foundation for even larger, full field-scale trials in the future.

Bennett, R M (Ed) (1989) *The 'greenhouse effect' and UK agriculture*. CAS Paper 19. Reading: Centre for Agricultural Strategy.

Poster presentation: Separating natural and manmade climate changes – implications for UK agriculture

B Denness

INTRODUCTION

Global temperature rose by 1.5°C in the middle of the last century *before* there was a 'greenhouse effect'. It dropped again by about 0.3°C between 1940 and 1970 *after* there was a greenhouse effect. This would totally undermine the popular current belief that the global warming of about 0.2°C over the last 20 years is due to the greenhouse effect *unless* it is recognised that the overall global temperature is dependent upon a natural component as well as the manmade element. Few would dispute this. However, major planning decisions – not least those affecting UK agriculture – are in the process of being taken with only the greenhouse effect in mind.

NATURAL AND MANMADE CLIMATE CHANGE

This note draws attention to an analytical means of deriving the variation of natural global temperature over all timescales in a deterministic way. Much of the background to the derivation of this mathematical model and its implications was given by Denness (1987). Figure 1 illustrates the subtraction of natural temperature (b), hindcast by the model, from the observed temperature (a) to leave the manmade element (c = a − b) for the last century. To ease interpretation this is subjected to smoothing by a 15-year moving average (the dotted line). The bold solid line which duplicates the mean through the moving average is identical to the greenhouse temperature change described by Hansen *et al* (1981) and many others (ie it simulates a rise of 3°C for a doubling of CO_2 in the atmosphere). The natural drop from 1940 to 1970 explains why the overall temperature

Figure 1
Separation of natural and manmade temperature change

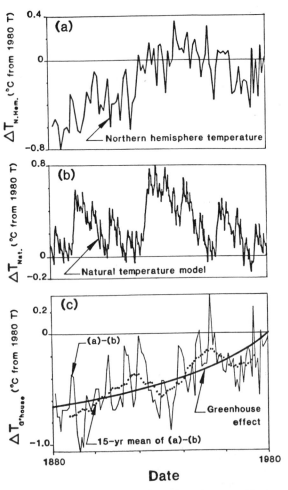

decreased then, even with an increasing greenhouse effect.

The addition of the greenhouse effect – essentially an ever-increasing phenomenon – this century appears to have had little influence in the UK or elsewhere. Changes in the natural global temperature may have far more impact on precipitation, agriculture and economies than does the greenhouse effect.

THE FUTURE

There are various agricultural implications which follow from the rise in temperature in the future. According to Wigley *et al* (1980) for instance, much of north-west Europe among many other regions, including the corn belt of the US, becomes drier as global temperature increases.

The combination of the natural and manmade components of the above model (successfully tested in forecasting mode since 1980) forecasts a global temperature rise of about 1°C in the 1990s, much higher than conventionally forecast. The repercussions for UK agriculture, sea-level rise and the global economy are very challenging.

REFERENCES

Denness, B (1987) Sea level modelling: the past and the future. *Prog. Oceanography*, **18**, 41–59.

Hansen, J, Johnson, D, Lacis, A, Lebedeff, A, Lees, P, Rind, D & Russell, G (1981) Climate impact of increasing atmospheric carbon dioxide. *Science*, **213**, 957–966.

Wigley, T M L, Jones, P D & Kelly, P M (1980) Scenario for a warm, high CO_2 world. *Nature*, **283**, 17–21.

Bennett, R M (Ed) (1989) *The 'greenhouse effect' and UK agriculture*. CAS Paper 19. Reading: Centre for Agricultural Strategy.

Poster presentation: The 'greenhouse effect' and effects on crop yields

R H Ellis, P Hadley, J I L Morison, E H Roberts & R J Summerfield

INTRODUCTION

A hierarchy of models is necessary to estimate the direct and indirect consequences of the 'greenhouse effect' on mankind's activities. First, to estimate the effect of increases in radiative-active gases within the atmosphere on climate both globally and regionally. Second, to assess the influence on agriculture of climatic changes in the different agro-ecological zones of the World, particularly on crop production. Third, to evaluate the outcome of changes in agricultural productivity on regional and national economies.

It follows that comprehensive studies of the greenhouse effect require a multi-disciplinary approach incorporating a hierarchy of quantitative models. This is also the case within the second sector above, estimating the influence of climate change on crop production.

Climatic models suggest that by the year 2050 carbon dioxide concentrations in the atmosphere may double, while mean global air temperatures could increase by 3–5°C. Crop yields depend on photosynthetic activity, developmental rate, physiological age, and the partitioning of photosynthate and nitrogen to harvestable yield.

Staff from three Departments at Reading have developed a series of quantitative models which describe various aspects of the influence of environment on crop growth and development. These models not only provide a means of assessing the impact of given changes in climate on crop production, but also a sound basis for developing genotypes better suited to the climate changes, to which we are already committed as a result of the historical rise in the concentration of the radiatively-active gases in the atmosphere.

PHOTOSYNTHESIS

Increased carbon dioxide concentrations directly affect plant growth through effects on photosynthesis, photorespiration, respiration and stomatal aperture. The process of principal concern is net photosynthesis. Plants with C3 photosynthetic pathways show increased net photosynthesis rates with an increase in CO_2 above present atmospheric concentrations, in contrast to C4 plants which show little change.

However, net photosynthesis is also influenced by temperature and irradiance and, crucially, by strong interactions between the effects of CO_2, irradiance and temperature. It is important, then, to quantify net photosynthesis in relation to variations in all three factors (ie as four-dimensional models). Nevertheless, it is clear that, at least for C3 plants grown in temperate latitudes, the predicted climatic changes are likely to increase net photosynthesis. For reasons discussed below, this trend may not necessarily lead to increased crop yields.

ACCLIMATION

There is substantial evidence that photosynthetic rate acclimates to raised CO_2 concentrations such that sustained net photosynthetic rates increase far less than short-term responses to CO_2 might suggest. The extent of acclimation to raised CO_2 concentrations may vary appreciably among crops.

ONTOGENY

Potential relative crop growth rate declines during ontogeny – it declines with physiological age. Physiological age is determined principally by thermal history (accumulated thermal time). Accordingly, the potential relative crop growth rate declines more rapidly in warmer conditions.

The potential relative crop growth rate at a given physiological age is modified by the current temperature and photosynthetic rate. It is essential to recognise the importance of ontogeny when studying the response of net photosynthesis to CO_2, irradiance and temperature. It also follows that it is necessary to distinguish between crops in terms of the effect of climate changes on yield depending upon the stage of ontogeny at which they are harvested (eg in root crops as distinct from grain crops).

PARTITIONING

There is evidence that the partitioning of assimilates – both carbon and nitrogen – can be influenced by relatively small differences in temperature.

For example, in several grain legume crops we have detected significant negative relations between Harvest Index and temperature over the range from 22 to 28°C. There is conflicting evidence concerning the effect of CO_2 on partitioning, perhaps because of the variety of crops and treatments investigated.

PHENOLOGY

Over a wide range of conditions in most crops, the rate of development and thus the duration of the vegetative phase – during which photosynthetic production capacity is determined – is a linear function of temperature and photoperiod. It follows that developmental times in fluctuating environments can be modelled in photothermal-time accumulated over the base temperature.

The phenotypic duration of any cultivar must match its intended agro-ecological zone. Warmer temperatures in the temperate latitudes will reduce the duration of a given cultivar which, since dry matter accumulation is a function of intercepted radiation, will reduce crop yields.

In the UK, for example, calculations based on the photothermal development model combined with field results from date-of-sowing investigations suggest that a 2°C increase in temperature may reduce grain yields of current spring cereal cultivars by approximately 15–20%.

The photothermal model can also be applied to characterise genotypes for their sensitivity of developmental rate to temperature and photoperiod. These studies have shown that the responses to each of these climatic variables are independent. And so the photothermal model provides a basis of screening and selecting genotypes which will match changed environments.

In contrast, phenology does not appear to be greatly affected by CO_2 concentration, although there is evidence of both increases and decreases in the rate of development resulting from raised CO_2 concentrations.

FUTURE RESEARCH

It seems clear that elevated CO_2 concentrations and warmer temperatures will raise, albeit briefly, net photosynthesis rates for young leaves of crop plants under optimum conditions. However, other considerations suggest that predicted benefits of the greenhouse effect to temperate agriculture, based simplistically on such responses, are unlikely to be realised, and that unless genotypes are developed which match the new climates, harvested yields from grain crops may decline. It follows that research intending to quantify the likely effects on crop production of changed CO_2 concentrations in the atmosphere and of the greenhouse effect, will need to combine studies on all the major variables, utilising controlled environments with varying degrees of sophistication (from pot-grown plants in growth cabinets to field-grown crops under plastic).

RECENT PUBLICATIONS

Ellis, R H, Hadley, P, Roberts, E H & Summerfield, R J (1990) Quantitative relations between temperature and crop development and growth. In: Jackson, M T, Ford-Lloyd, B V & Parry, M L (Eds) *Climate changes and plant genetic resources*. London: Belhaven Press. (In press).

Morison, J I L (1985) Sensitivity of stomata and water use efficiency to high CO_2. *Plant Cell and Environment*, **8**, 467–74.

Morison, J I L (1988) Effect of increasing CO_2 on plants and their responses to other pollutants, climatic and soil factors. *Aspects of Applied Biology*, **17**, 113–22.

Morison, J I L (1989) Plant growth in increased atmospheric carbon dioxide. In: Fantechi, R & Ghazi, A (Eds) *Carbon dioxide and other greenhouse gases: climatic and associated impacts*. Dordrecht: Kluwer Academic Publishers.

Roberts, E H & Summerfield, R J (1987) Measurement and prediction of flowering in annual crops. In: Atherton, J G (Ed) *Manipulation of flowering*. London: Butterworths.

Bennett, R M (Ed) (1989) *The 'greenhouse effect' and UK agriculture.* CAS Paper 19. Reading: Centre for Agricultural Strategy.

Poster presentation: Carbon storage by forests and forest products

R Matthews

INTRODUCTION

Since the beginning of this century, the Forestry Commission has maintained an array of intensively measured permanent sample plots throughout Britain, which give information on the timber volume production of plantation forests. By taking a few extra measurements, it is possible to use sample plot data to estimate the amount of carbon being fixed from the atmosphere by trees.

RESEARCH METHOD AND RESULTS

Samples of wood were taken from a series of points on the stems of plot trees. The green density and dry mass were measured, and the carbon content estimated by chemical analysis. The main results are summarised in Table 1 below.

Table 1

Carbon content of trees from five permanent sample plots

	Green density t/m^3	Dry mass/ wet mass	Carbon per unit dry mass t/m^3	Carbon per unit green vol t/m^3
Oak, Forest of Dean	0.80	0.70	0.46	0.26
Birch, Easter Ross	0.49	0.68	0.46	0.15
Corsican pine, Thetford	0.31	0.66	0.48	0.10
Sitka spruce, N Lakes	0.36	0.67	0.48	0.12
Sitka spruce, N Yorks	0.38	0.66	0.47	0.12

The figure for carbon per unit dry mass is remarkably constant at around 0.47. However, wood density varies significantly between species and also varies within the stem of each tree, generally being lower in the younger wood. The change in wood density with age means that carbon per unit volume also varies, but further study is required to characterise this change. Combining these results with sample plot timber volume information, gives a picture of the rate of carbon fixing by the sample trees. Figures 1 and 2

Figure 1
Carbon fixed by unthinned Sitka spruce plantation, Dalby Forest, North Yorkshire

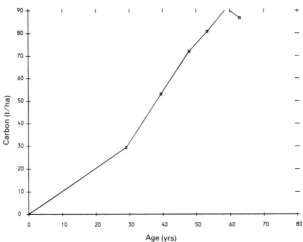

Figure 2
Carbon fixed by oak plantation, Forest of Dean

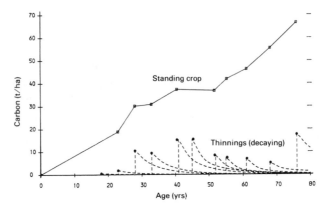

illustrate the rate at which carbon is being fixed by the plots in North Yorkshire and the Forest of Dean respectively.

When timber is harvested, by thinning or felling, the wood does not release its carbon at once. At present, there is little data available on lifespans of timber products but, using information on timber markets and industry practices, it is possible to build a model to predict the utilisation of harvested wood and its subsequent decay. A utilisation and decay model has been used to predict the decay of thinnings from the oak plot shown in Figure 2.

Permanent sample plot data has also been used to construct yield models for most major British plantation species. These are used to forecast timber volume production in British forests. The models may be adapted to forecast future rates of carbon fixing, and also to assess the consequences of different systems of forest management and changes in the utilisation of the timber produced. For example, Figure 3 is a simulation of the cumulative effect of three rotations of a typical Sitka spruce plantation, allowing for utilisation of the timber.

Figure 3
Sitka spruce yield Class 12. Simulated carbon production and decay over 3 rotations

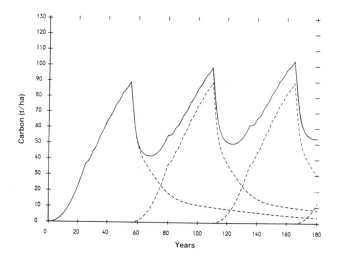

Bennett, R M (Ed) (1989) *The 'greenhouse effect' and UK agriculture.* CAS Paper 19. Reading: Centre for Agricultural Strategy.

Poster presentation: Vegetation and the 'greenhouse effect'

I McKee

INTRODUCTION

Man's activities have resulted in a substantial increase in the atmospheric concentration of CO_2 over pre-industrial levels. It is predicted that this concentration may have doubled by the middle of the next century.

CO_2 has the capacity to absorb and re-radiate long-wave radiation so the effect of rising levels of atmospheric CO_2 on the 'global radiation budget' is to cause a rise in global mean surface air temperature – the so-called 'greenhouse effect'.

Predictions of the mean rise in temperature consistent with a doubling of the atmospheric CO_2 concentration range between 1.5 and 5.5°C. Latitudinal variation in the radiation budget implies significantly greater warming towards the poles than at the equator.

Both ambient temperature and atmospheric CO_2 concentration have profound effects on plant physiology and thereby on global vegetation patterns. A programme of computer modelling exercises and growth-chamber experiments is underway at Cambridge to investigate the interaction of these effects.

THE COMPUTER MODELLING APPROACH

The type of natural vegetation found in any particular region is controlled by, and interacts with, the temperature regime and rainfall pattern. Rainfall over a plant canopy is taken up by the roots and is lost via the leaves. The greater the leaf area the more rapid the loss. Although excess water is stored in vegetation and soil, if loss exceeds gain for too long the deficit results in wilting and ultimately death. The leaf area index (m^2 of leaf per m^2 of ground) of a vegetation stand is therefore limited by the rate of precipitation. Of course the rate of water loss rises with increasing temperature, so hotter climates require more rainfall to support the same leaf area index.

Given a range of climatic factors, the maximum permitted leaf area index can be predicted for any site, and related to the appropriate vegetation type. This calculation forms the first step in any computer model designed to predict changes in vegetation distribution in response to a changing climate.

Minimum temperatures are critical to plant survival. Different physiognomic types of vegetation are resistant to different degrees of chilling and vary in frost tolerance (eg the needles of a boreal conifer survive lower temperatures than the buds of a temperate broadleaf-deciduous tree, which in turn survive lower temperatures than the leaves of a Mediterranean broadleaf evergreen). Many conifers show no observable limit to frost tolerance whereas water-melon plants show chilling responses at 15°C. Minimum temperatures and frequency of severe winters must therefore be taken into account in computer predictions of vegetation type.

In both seasonally arid and seasonally cold climates the length of growing season may be a limiting factor for plant survival. If we combine this constraint with the two previously outlined (hydrological budget and minimum temperature) we can generate a computer model able to predict vegetation from climatic data. With the aid of a physiologically based computer model such as this the global vegetation pattern for today may be predicted (Figure 1). A comparison of this prediction with the actual natural vegetation found around the World shows that the model has good predictive power.

Figure 1
Computer model prediction of global vegetation now

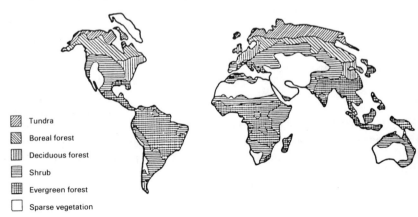

Tundra

Boreal forest

Deciduous forest

Shrub

Evergreen forest

Sparse vegetation

Using climatologists' computer predictions of global climate in a 'greenhouse world', with doubled atmospheric CO_2 concentration, and the computer vegetation model, the vegetation patterns for the next century may be predicted as shown in Figure 2. This prediction assumes rapid plant migration on a vast scale which is, in many areas and for many species, not possible. Without man's intervention extinctions would seem inevitable.

Figure 2
Computer model predictions of vegetation in a 'greenhouse world'

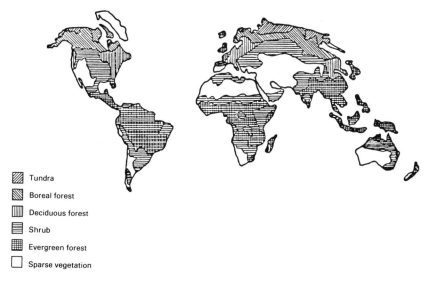

▨ Tundra
▨ Boreal forest
▥ Deciduous forest
▤ Shrub
▦ Evergreen forest
☐ Sparse vegetation

Computer predictions of this sort provide important information for foresters and agronomists and provide an extraordinary challenge for conservationists.

The experimental programme currently in progress at the Cambridge Department of Botany aims to explore the direct effects of CO_2 on plant growth, and interactions with other environmental factors. This allows us to improve and expand our computer models of 'greenhouse world' vegetation and hopefully to answer the important questions posed by industry, forestry, agriculture and conservation bodies in relation to plants and the greenhouse effect.

Bennett, R M (Ed) (1989) *The 'greenhouse effect' and UK agriculture*. CAS Paper 19. Reading: Centre for Agricultural Strategy.

Poster presentation: Interactions between climate change and nitrate leaching using the AFRC model of winter wheat growth

J R Porter

MODEL AND SCENARIOS

An outline of the AFRC Wheat Model is shown in Figure 1.

Figure 1

An outline of the AFRC Wheat Model showing the submodels for (i) phenological development (ii) canopy development (iii) CO_2 exchange, dry-matter production and partitioning (iv) environmental modifiers of the above crop processes

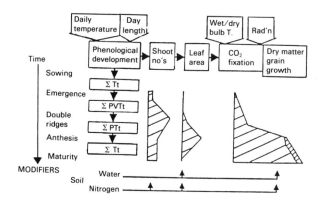

The model was run using 4 scenarios of climate change:

1. Baseline – simulation of a crop grown at Rothamsted Experimental Station in 1985; well irrigated and adequately supplied with nutrients. Present-day CO_2 and temperature.
2. Baseline with a X2 CO_2 level and a 4°C increase in mean daily temperature throughout the season. *No change in rainfall.*
3. Baseline with a X2 CO_2 level and a 4°C increase in mean daily temperature and with a 40% *increase* (above observed) in rainfall September–February and with 40% *decrease* in rainfall March–August (wet winter/dry summer).
4. Baseline with a X2 CO_2 level and a 4°C increase in mean daily temperature and with a 40% *increase* (above observed) in rainfall throughout the season (wet winter/wet summer).

RESULTS

Table 1 below shows the results for these scenarios.

Table 1
Results from running the model for the 4 scenarios

			SCENARIO			
			1	2	3	4
CROP GROWTH						
Total crop weight (DM) at maturity (t/ha)			19.4	23.5	20.6	22.5
Grain yield (t/ha)			9.4	7.0	7.1	7.1
Harvest Index (%)			48	30	34	31
NITROGEN/NITRATE BALANCE (kg/ha)						
Input:	mineralised	N	51		51	58
	fertilizer	N	154		154	154
	soil residual	N	27		27	26
	Total	N	232		232	238
Output:	plant uptake	N	226		216	223
	drainage	N (NO_3)	6 (26)		16 (70)	15 (66)
	Total	N	232		232	238

This points to the following:
  (i)   Results for the simple increase in temperature and CO_2 (scenario 2) are much in line with previous simulations (ie total crop DM not much affected but grain yield decreased).
  (ii) In scenario 3 over 2X as much N/ha was leached. From deeper analysis of the output it is clear that this was because the warmer, wetter winter allowed most mineralisation to occur in the soil. Also, since the crop was not in the soil for the same length of time as the non-greenhouse one, due to higher temperatures and thus faster development more N leached through.
  (iii) The combination of a greenhouse climate of a wet winter with a wet summer (scenario 4) also results in more N leaching.

IMPLICATIONS

The model output points to possible serious agricultural problems from the interaction between nitrate leaching, associated pollution and climate change. Further studies in this area are required, performed in conjunction with modelling work.

Bennett, R M (Ed) (1989) *The 'greenhouse effect' and UK agriculture*. CAS Paper 19. Reading: Centre for Agricultural Strategy.

Poster presentation: Modelling greenhouse gas-induced climate change

P R Rowntree, B A Callander & J Cochrane

INTRODUCTION

Surface observations of air temperature since 1900 are consistent with an enhanced greenhouse effect (see Figure 1) – although they do not prove it.

Figure 1
Global surface air temperature relative to 1950–79 average

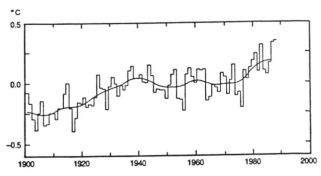

Source: Derived from Jones *et al* (1988).

The 20th century has seen an average increase of 0.5°C in mean global temperature. But the increase has not been steady. There is considerable variation from year to year, and from decade to decade. For example, the period 1940–70 was one of cooling, even though there was an increase in the release of greenhouse gases.

MODELS

Mathematical models of climate, on the other hand, agree that global warming over the next century is almost inevitable. Basic laws of physics imply that increased CO_2 and other greenhouse gases should lead to global warming, but we need mathematical models of climate to estimate how far temperatures will rise. The answers given by models depend to some extent on the feedback mechanisms which they incorporate.

Equilibrium models predict climate once the whole atmosphere and oceans have responded fully to, say, a doubling of CO_2 concentrations (see Table 1). Transient models take account of the steady increase of greenhouse gases year by year, and of the time taken by the ocean, particularly the deep ocean, to warm up. Transient models provide predictions of the temperature rises we are likely to experience over the next 50–100 years (see Figure 2).

Table 1
Total warming due to the doubling of CO_2

	Process	Total warming (°C)
	Doubling of CO_2	1.2
Add	Increased water vapour	1.7
Add	Reduction of snow and ice cover	2.2
Add	Changes in type and amount of cloud	2.0–5.0

Figure 2
Global mean temperatures 1850–2100 from a one-dimensional model

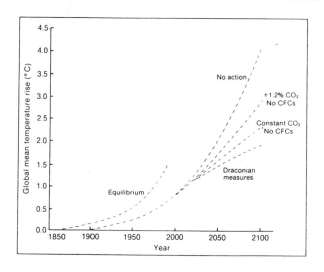

113

SOME POTENTIAL IMPACTS ON AGRICULTURE OF A 2°C WARMING

Fewer frosts

Figure 3 shows the potential impact on minimum January temperature.

Figure 3
Potential impact of a 2°C warming on minimum January temperature

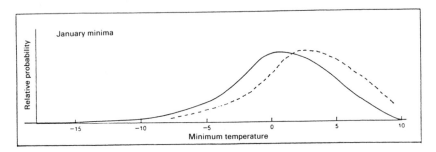

Sea level changes

Global sea level rise from the present to 2040 is likely to be in the range 20 to 50 cm.

Earlier start to the growing season

The start of the growing season is taken as the date on which mean 30 cm soil temperature exceeds 6°C. A mean 2°C rise in temperature would bring that date forward in England and Wales by between 2 and 3 weeks, depending on distance from the coast. Figure 4 shows the potentially earlier growing season by area, with a 2°C temperature rise.

Increased evaporation

In the UK, and particularly in winter, humidity and temperature have a greater effect on evapotranspiration (PT) than sunshine and windspeed. The graphs in Figure 5, based on data from a site in the East Midlands, show mean annual progress charts under a 2°C warmer climate, for potential soil moisture deficit (PT minus rainfall) and for drainage into the soil (rainfall minus PT).

Figure 4
The potential earlier start to the growing season in England and Wales, following a 2°C temperature rise.

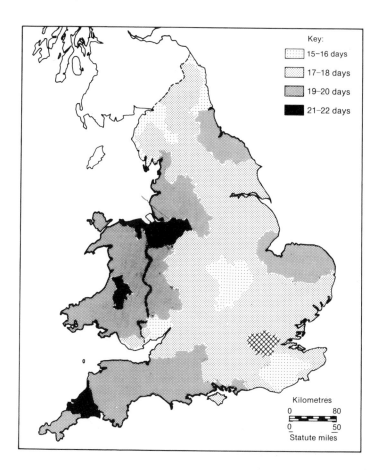

Key:
- 15–16 days
- 17–18 days
- 19–20 days
- 21–22 days

Kilometres
0   80
0   50
Statute miles

Figure 5
Mean annual progress charts for potential soil moisture deficit and for drainage into the soil, under a 2°C warmer climate.

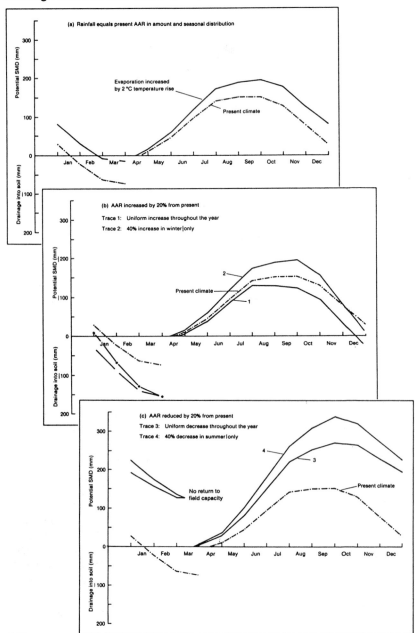

Bennett, R M (Ed) (1989) *The 'greenhouse effect' and UK
agriculture.* CAS Paper 19. Reading: Centre for Agricultural
Strategy.

Poster presentation: Climatic change and UK agriculture

G R Squire, M H Unsworth, J S Cox, J Craigon & D Stokes

INTRODUCTION

In 1988 a review termed 'Effects of CO_2 and climatic change in agriculture'
was produced for the DOE by G R Squire and M H Unsworth. The Review
considers the possible impact of climatic change on UK agriculture as a
result of the 'greenhouse effect', based upon a literature survey and
computer models.

THE DOE REVIEW

The main conclusions of the Review are as follows.

(i)   Temperature affects plant development and growth, the populations
      of plant pests and diseases, and the performance of farm animals. A
      3°C rise in temperature would cause crops to develop faster, leading
      to lower yields in determinate crops such as cereals, and higher
      yields of indeterminate crops such as sugar beet and grasses.

(ii) Effects of CO_2 on crop plants have been studied largely in controlled
      environment chambers which do not adequately simulate the field.
      Raising the CO_2 concentration increases the rate of photosynthesis
      and the production of dry matter in these artificial systems. On
      average, a doubling of CO_2 causes a 30% increase in dry matter and
      yield. It also improves the return of yield from applying a given
      amount of water. However, it is not clear whether these responses
      are lost in some species as plants acclimate, or whether the benefits
      of increased CO_2 would be so large in stands of crops growing in
      natural conditions.

The interaction of CO_2 and temperature was examined using mathematical models of yield for winter wheat and potato. The models assumed the short-term responses of crops in controlled environments were representative of those in the field. If CO_2 doubled, but temperature was unchanged, the potential yield achievable by cultivars currently grown in the UK would increase by about 25% for both species, provided water, nutrients, pests and diseases were not limiting. A concurrent increase in temperature of 3 to 4°C would completely counter the enhancement due to CO_2 for wheat (see Figure 1), but would amplify that for potato, such that yield would increase by 50% to 75% of the present value.

Figure 1
Potential yield of winter wheat[1]

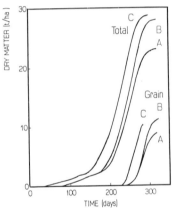

1 Modelled responses of total dry matter production and grain yield of winter wheat using the AFRC model. A shows curves modelled from the 1981 climatic conditions at Brooms Barn, Bury St Edmonds; B simulates the effect of a doubling of carbon dioxide concentration; and C, the effect of both a doubled carbon dioxide concentration and a rise in mean temperature of 3°C.

(iii) Rainfall influences many processes of crop production, both through its effect on the amount and movement of water in soils, and on the dryness of the atmosphere. A decrease in rainfall, particularly in summer in much of the UK arable farmland area, would reduce yields considerably. These reductions would arise partly from a lack of soil water, and partly from a restriction imposed on growth by the associated drier air. Wider and more extensive use of irrigation, which would hardly raise the atmospheric humidity, could only partly reverse the effects of low rainfall. An increase in rainfall, especially in winter, would increase the loss of nitrate fertilizer from the soil, and reduce the period in autumn when land was suitable for vehicular access and cultivation. With the present scenarios for climatic change, there is considerable uncertainty about both the size of the expected change in atmospheric humidity, and the effects of this change on crop growth and the population of pests and diseases. Also, the costs and constraints imposed by the use of more fertilizer and the reduced access to land cannot be estimated reliably.

(iv) Interactions between temperature, humidity and rainfall will have substantial effects on epidemiology of pests and diseases, which would call for adaptations to the application of pesticides, at least in the timing and degree of control required.

The observed times taken for winter wheat to reach key developmental stages during winter/spring 1988/89 were compared to those predicted by the AFRC wheat model (see Figure 2). The wheat model performs well, despite the relatively high winter temperatures (1–2°C above average). This illustrates the potential usefulness of models that are capable of predicting the effects of climatic change on UK agricultural enterprises.

FURTHER WORK

The DOE have commissioned a further report to assess the impact of the relatively mild 1988/89 winter temperatures on British agriculture and horticulture. Information is currently being collected and collated on the following topics.

(i) The growth and yield of arable crops.
(ii) Grass growth and associated animal enterprises.
(iii) The timing, quality and yield of vegetables including glasshouse winter crops.
(iv) Phenology of top and soft fruit.
(v) The incidence of pathogens, pests and weed problems.
(vi) Changes in management practices.

The report will be completed by October 1989.

Figure 2
Winter wheat development in the mild winter 1988/89[1]

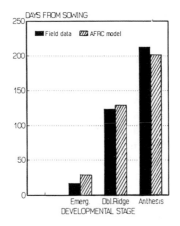

1 The observed time taken for winter wheat*, grown at Sutton Bonington, to reach key developmental stages is compared with predictions based on the AFRC Wheat Model. The wheat model performs well even under the relatively high winter temperatures of 1988/89.

* Data courtesy of J Craigon and D Stokes, using cv Mercia sown on 19/11/1988.

REFERENCE
Squire, G R & Unsworth, M H (1988) *Effects of CO_2 and climate change in agriculture*. Research Report. Department of Physiology and Environmental Science, University of Nottingham.

Bennett, R M (Ed) (1989) *The 'greenhouse effect' and UK agriculture*. CAS Paper 19. Reading: Centre for Agricultural Strategy.

Poster presentation: Possible consequences of the 'greenhouse effect' for the spring growth of *Lolium Perenne*

N Sweet

INTRODUCTION

The possible consequences for agriculture of climatic changes due to the greenhouse effect are currently a major scientific concern. Cereals and grasses are probably the most important crop plants, with grasslands alone covering approximately one quarter of the earth's surface. In the UK, grass is a very important crop, and any environmental factor affecting the production from grassland will have a significant impact on UK agriculture, and have major economic consequences.

In the spring, following vernalisation, the perennial grass sward changes from vegetative to reproductive development, and a number of well-documented physiological changes occur in the grass plant (Pollock & Jones, 1979). These enable the high and sustained rates of dry matter (DM) production characteristics of the spring sward. It is during this period that potential growth rates of grass are highest (Parsons & Robson, 1980), and therefore environmental changes will have maximum effect.

MATERIALS AND METHODS

A greenhouse experiment was set up using seedlings of *Lolium perenne* cv. Frances, transplanted from an autumn sown field on 17 December 1987. These were potted in Levington Professional compost, 5 plants per 4 in square plastic pot. Two controlled environment greenhouses were used, with an additional adjacent outside treatment area to give three treatments with different rates of temperature accumulation:

    (i)   Outside, ambient conditions;

121

(ii) Ventilated greenhouse;

(iii) Unventilated greenhouse.

Air temperature and soil temperature at a depth of 1 cm were measured using copper-constantan thermocouples. Both were logged using a Cambell 21X data logger, which recorded measurements once every minute. Hourly means were calculated from the data by the logger and stored. The development of the plants was monitored by recording apical development at approximately 25 day degrees (d°C) intervals. Growth analysis measurements were made at 50 d°C intervals.

RESULTS

Figure 1 shows the resulting time courses of thermal time (day degrees above 0°C) accumulation for each treatment. The experiment produced temperatures in the closed greenhouse on average 3°C above those outside, a difference of the same order as the warming predicted by some models of the greenhouse effect (Dickinson & Cicerone, 1986). The temperature difference between the two greenhouse treatments was only 1°C, and the differences in the rates of accumulation of thermal time were not significant.

Figure 2 shows the corresponding time courses of leaf area expansion for the closed greenhouse and the outside treatment. Leaf area expanded much earlier inside than outside. Plants from the greenhouse treatment at the same developmental stage as those outside had a significantly larger leaf area. The differences in the rates of accumulation between the two greenhouse treatments were not significant.

CONCLUSIONS

In temperate climates, temperature determines the length of the growing season for crops as well as that of the grazing season for animals. Although development may be triggered by vernalisation, temperature controls the subsequent timing of developmental processes, such as the rates of leaf expansion, and so controls the period for which a crop canopy effectively intercepts solar radiation. There may also be a smaller temperature effect on the efficiency with which solar radiation is used to make DM (Montieth & Scott, 1982). For an indeterminate crop, such as grass, the duration of the canopy and the cumulative intercepted radiation should increase with increasing temperatures, because the canopy is formed sooner and the growing season is longer than at low temperatures. However, optimum Leaf Area Index (LAI) for dry matter production is strongly influenced by the level of solar radiation received, as well as by the temperature, water and nutrient regimes of the crop.

Figure 1
Day degrees v Julian Days

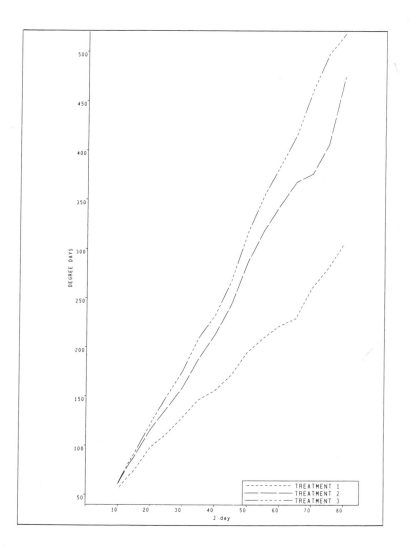

Figure 2
Leaf area v Julian Day

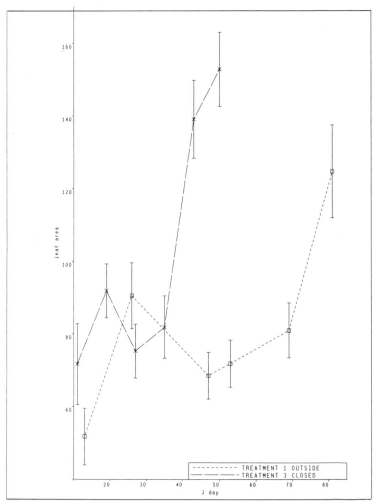

The results of this experiment clearly show that a warming of 3°C will significantly accelerate the spring leaf area expansion of a *L. perenne* sward. This could have a marked effect on farming practices, in that DM targets for 'turn-out' may be reached at an earlier date than in the current climate. The overall effect of temperature on seasonal dry matter production is governed mainly by the effect on intercepted radiation. Light interception by a cut or grazed sward will be reduced, but solar radiation levels later in the season will be higher. If the regrowth of the sward is also accelerated by the warmer temperatures, dry matter production should also be greater, provided that the water and nutrient status of the crop remain optimal.

ACKNOWLEDGEMENTS
The author wishes to thank Dr J A Clark, Dr C K Baker and Dr B Callander for their help and encouragement with this work. The author holds a MAFF/Meteorological Office CASE postgraduate studentship.

REFERENCES
Dickinson, R E & Cicerone, R J (1986) Future global warming from atmospheric trace gases. *Nature,* **319**, 109–115.

Montieth, J L & Scott, R K (1982) Weather and yield variation in crops. In: Blaxter, K & Fowden, L (Eds) *Food nutrition and climate*. London: Applied Science.

Parsons, A J & Robson, M J (1980) Seasonal changes in the physiology of S24 perennial rye grass (Lolium perenne L); 1. response of leaf extension to temperature during the transition from vegetative to reproductive growth. *Annals of Botany,* **46**, 435–444.

Pollock, C J & Jones T (1979) Seasonal patterns of fructan metabolism in forage grasses. *New Phytologist,* **83**, 9–15.

Bennett, R M (Ed) (1989) *The 'greenhouse effect' and UK agriculture*. CAS Paper 19. Reading: Centre for Agricultural Strategy.

Poster presentation: The effects of climate change on wheat yields: sensitivity of model predictions to increases in cloud cover

R Mitchell

INTRODUCTION

Crop models provide a means of assessing the impact of climate change on yields. Since the extent of changes in temperature, cloud and precipitation that will occur in the UK for a given rise in atmospheric CO_2 are uncertain, simulations need to be carried out over a wide range of these conditions. We used a model of winter wheat to simulate the effects of possible combinations of changes in CO_2, temperature and cloud on yields.

DESCRIPTION OF MODEL

The model was composed of:

 (i) a mechanistic model of canopy photosynthesis modified from that of Spitters (1986);

 (ii) phenological development and grain growth modules similar to those in the AFRCWHEAT model (Weir *et al*, 1984);

 (iii) a model of leaf growth which uses available assimilate as an input.

A wheat crop grown in 1985 at Rothamsted was used as the starting point for simulations. Yields were modelled for:

 (i) increases in CO_2 of up to 80 ppm combined with increases in temperature of up to $+2.5°C$;

 (ii) a constant CO_2 concentration of 430 ppm (corresponding to the predicted value for the year 2030, temperature increases of up to $+2.5°C$ combined with cloud cover increases of up to 15%.

Figure 1
Response surface of model predictions of wheat yield for increases in temperature and atmospheric CO_2 concentration over 1985 conditions. (Yields are expressed as % change from a 1985 crop.)

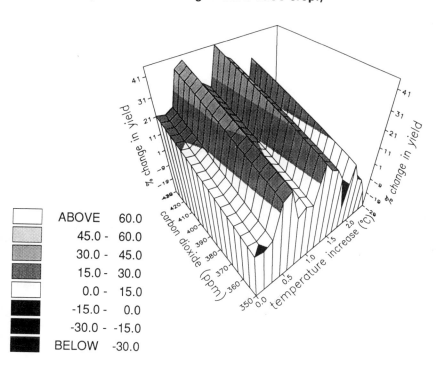

ABOVE 60.0
45.0 - 60.0
30.0 - 45.0
15.0 - 30.0
0.0 - 15.0
-15.0 - 0.0
-30.0 - -15.0
BELOW -30.0

RESULTS AND CONCLUSION

The results of simulations in Figure 1 show that increased CO_2 concentrations are always beneficial, with a rise of 80 ppm increasing yield by 15–20%. The effect of temperature is more complex. At certain temperature increases, the model predicts the appearance of extra leaves, which lead to sharply increased yields. However, the shortened grain-filling period and increased respiration cause decreasing yields with increasing temperatures between peaks. Temperature increases greater than +2°C result in a net decrease in yield relative to 1985 conditions.

Figure 2 shows that the model predicts that increasing cloud cover greatly decreases yields. An increase of 5–10% in cloud is sufficient to completely negate any positive effects of increased CO_2 and temperature. Any assessment of the impact of climate change on UK agriculture must therefore take into account possible changes in cloud.

Figure 2
Response surface of wheat yield predicted by model for increases in temperature and cloud over 1985 conditions, at an elevated CO_2 concentration of 430 ppm.
(Yields are expressed as % change from a 1985 crop.)

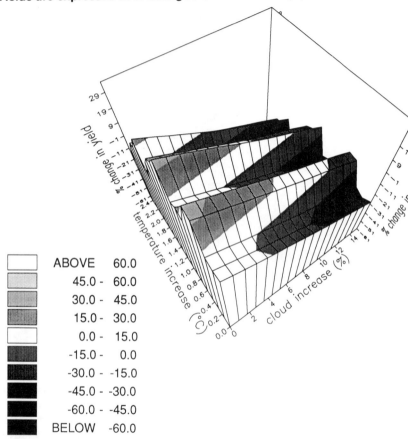

ABOVE	60.0
45.0 -	60.0
30.0 -	45.0
15.0 -	30.0
0.0 -	15.0
-15.0 -	0.0
-30.0 -	-15.0
-45.0 -	-30.0
-60.0 -	-45.0
BELOW	-60.0

REFERENCES
Spitters, C J T (1986) Separating the diffuse and direct components of global radiation and its implications for modelling canopy photosynthesis. Part II: Calculation of canopy photosynthesis. *Agricultural and Forest Meteorology*, **38**, 231–242.
Weir, A H, Bragg, P L, Porter, J R & Rayner, J H (1984) A winter wheat crop simulation model without water or nutrient limitations. *Journal of Agricultural Science, Cambridge*, **102**, 371–382.

Discussion summary

Bennett, R M (Ed) (1989) *The 'greenhouse effect' and UK agriculture*. CAS Paper 19. Reading: Centre for Agricultural Strategy.

Summary of discussion during the Conference

Chairman: C R W Spedding
Rapporteur: J C Tayler

GENERAL DISCUSSION

Mr Phillip Needham, Director of the Farm and Countryside Service of ADAS, opened the general discussion. He said that farmers in the UK had already shown their ability to respond to changes and had adapted to changing circumstances rapidly over the last decade or two in response to economic and political signals.

Although there had been broad agreement among the speakers on the long-term trend of increase in temperature, there was still a major uncertainty about quantity and distribution of rainfall, which is crucial for agriculture. We had heard about the drift northwards in crop limits but before having visions of the Cairngorms ablaze with sunflowers we should remember the important effects of altitude, topography, soil properties and the rural infrastructure, as well as market factors of social and economic criteria which would influence the actual response of the farming industry. Ecology would determine what *may* be done but politics will determine what *will* be done. For the northern temperate zone, the range of possibilities open to the farming industry would be widened, and this should be a benefit.

Three questions could be raised on behalf of farmers:

(i) What is the effect on the competitive position of the farmer, in different parts of the UK, relative to the EC and the World as a whole, and how can he take advantage of any changes?

(ii) What annual variations in weather can be expected?

(iii) Given the timescale and the elasticity of the timescales discussed, is there anything realistic that a farmer can do at this stage in terms of forward planning, particularly of capital investment?

The following issues were raised and discussed during the discussion periods following each paper presentation and during the general discussion after all the papers had been presented. These issues are summarised under general headings rather than recorded verbatim.

THE 'GREENHOUSE EFFECT' IN PERSPECTIVE

The first paper had placed the 'greenhouse effect' in the perspective of the earth's climatic history over 850 000 years. The meteorologists in the audience added further comment on current levels of CO_2. The CO_2 concentration is now at about 350 ppm, which is higher than at any time in the last 140 000 years, but it is expected to reach levels of 600 ppm (well outside the range experienced in the last million years) within the next few decades.

Continental drift can complicate the interpretation of geological data, but there is a useful indication to be derived from the tropical carboniferous fossil flora at the latitude of Ellesmere Island, which has been at 85°N for a very long time, showing that CO_2 levels were 4–6 times those of the present. Furthermore, a clear distinction should be made between the transient temperature response to a doubling of CO_2 by the year 2030, giving an increase of 3.2°C, and the time at which the climate would be in equilibrium with this increase, which would take 40–50 years longer. Even if the present increase in greenhouse gases was to cease now, a residual warming of about 0.5°C would occur.

The assumption that the greenhouse effect results mainly from man's activities since the Industrial Revolution was queried. It was admitted that it is difficult to distinguish the effect of these activities from natural changes and trends. However, what can be affirmed is that there are changes in atmospheric composition which are far beyond any that the earth has experienced in the past, and changes in temperature appear to coincide with what would be predicted by model simulation from these atmospheric changes.

CONTRIBUTORS TO THE 'GREENHOUSE EFFECT'
Agriculture

A question was raised on the contribution of nitrogen fertilizers to the greenhouse effect. It had been claimed that some 2% of the effect is contributed by nitrous oxide (N_2O), and that a considerable part of this comes from agriculture. Figures given for N_2O arising from the use of fertilizers seem excessive, particularly since there is no reliable method at present for measuring N_2O production from fields. Professor Treharne responded that nitrous oxide is produced by the process of denitrification in the soil – a process that is temperature-dependent. If the soil is ploughed for arable agriculture, firstly, mineralisation (converting organic nitrogen into inorganic nitrogen, which is taken up by the crop) is increased. Secondly, denitrification (conversion of nitrate to nitrite and the release of N_2O) is increased. In view of the increase in land devoted to arable production over the last 40 years, the figure of 2% could be of the right order. The effect will be dependent on the level of nitrogen in the system which can be affected both by fertilizer use and manure use.

A general conclusion from this discussion was that some of the greenhouse gases such as methane and nitrous oxide are produced as a result of agriculture, and the agricultural industry worldwide may be required to do something about the use of ruminants, boglands, paddyfields and fertilizers.

Deforestation and afforestation
Deforestation has historically been an important factor and will continue to have an effect, but it will probably be outweighed by increases in the use of energy from fossil fuels. Primeval forest is in a state of equilibrium between respiration (and decay) and carbon fixation. Burning of rain forest not only adds a burst of CO_2 into the atmosphere, but leaching of nutrients from the soil reduces herbaceous regrowth and therefore the photosynthetic capacity of the deforested area.

Afforestation had been proposed as a palliative. However, calculations on the effect of planting forests to absorb CO_2 emissions have suggested that an ameliorating effect of no more than 10% could be achieved on the rate of increase of CO_2 resulting from the use of fossil fuels.

ACTIONS TO LIMIT THE INCREASE IN 'GREENHOUSE' GASES
Chlorofluorocarbons
Chlorofluorocarbons are important contributors to the greenhouse effect (as well as to ozone depletion) and international action is being taken to limit the use of these. Since the effect of these chemicals is so great, the possibility of recycling them was suggested. This was seen to have practical difficulties. In addition to their use as refrigerants, many other uses, such as in cleaning agents, are responsible for their unrecoverable release into the atmosphere.

SPECIFIC 'GREENHOUSE EFFECTS'
Regional effects
Taking a global view, effects are greater at the poles than at the equator. The effects expected are melting of the edge of the ice zones, the receding of

glaciers and a greater exposure of tundra regions. This will produce a major change from an ice or snow surface to a land or sea surface, which can have considerable feedback effects in the models.

In the UK, rainfall shortage would be likely to cause a westward shift in the distribution of the population. Already the supplies of potable water in the south-east of Britain are at limiting values, and the pressures of urban populations wishing to move would have considerable effects on agriculture.

It was concluded, however, that the most important impact on UK agriculture may be from effects in other world zones. Shortage of water when temperatures are increased would cause limitations to growth of crops elsewhere, which may increase pressures for their production in the UK.

Wind, rainfall, soil erosion

Wind has a considerable effect on livestock, tree planting, vegetation, evaporation, and erosion, but the effect of a warming of the atmosphere on wind is at present unpredictable. There are indications of probable increased frequencies in convective thunderstorms and tropical cyclones.

Little had been said by the speakers about the effect of lower rainfall and the need to conserve moisture. However, in a scenario assuming a shortage of rainfall this would be a critical issue which would affect the cost of ensuring an adequate water supply, not only for agriculture, but also for the many uses of water by urban populations.

Soil erosion could be a greater problem through the introduction of erodable crops such as maize, soybeans and sugar beet, or an increase in the area devoted to them. Furthermore, both a higher winter rainfall and the more widespread application of irrigation could increase soil erosion. Afforestation could be used to counteract these soil losses.

Grassland

Effects of the greenhouse effect on grassland received considerable discussion since grass covers two thirds of the surface of the UK and is of great importance to UK agriculture. Questions were raised on the main effect of climatic changes on white clover pastures and on the expected difficulty of grassland management. One view was that the expected temperature changes would increase the length of the growing period for grassland and so increase yield, but probably by no more than about 5%. Difficulties of management arising from the longer growing season are likely to be concerned with the effects of poaching in spring, of drought in mid-summer and of reduced nutritional value in the autumn. It was thought that the effects on clover-rich swards would be similar, and a move towards clover swards in the future was likely. These managerial aspects are likely to be important and to depend more on factors such as rainfall distribution, nitrogen flux and differences between years, than on a difference of 3°C in temperature over a period of 50 years.

Alternative views were also expressed. Professor Stoddart (AFRC, Institute for Grassland and Animal Production) suggested that a more prolonged growing season for grass, which could increase to 8–10 months of the year, would have limitations of utilisation in specific situations – for example, on heavy land with large livestock where poaching may occur, but these could readily be overcome by a change of management. An earlier start to grazing would be an advantage, since the best quality herbage is produced early in the spring. Clover starts growth relatively late in the season and this would be improved by an increase in temperature, leading to increased use of grass/clover swards and reduced costs of production.

At a higher altitude, earlier grassland growth would give substantial benefits. Increases in arable area had been predicted but the terrain and soil type in large parts of the country are only suitable for grassland and animal production. Short-term rotation may be needed for animal production and grass growth. Professor Stoddart added that where growth cannot be maintained through the year, grass reserves of stored carbon are important for persistence and subsequent production. With good reserves, grass can sustain higher growth in early season at low radiation levels. In winter, at higher temperatures, grass could respire to death. Examples from single species swards should not be the sole means of predicting effects on grassland production in general.

Energy costs, buildings
In contrast to the positive economic impacts attributed to the greenhouse effect it was suggested that there may well be increased energy costs, for example increased demand for air conditioning and hence for electricity, reaching a peak in the summer. Some scenarios suggest increased variability in the weather pattern, so that variation round $0°C$ may be more important than degree-days. There may be less demand for insulation in buildings but there could be an effect, in terms of drying-out of clay soils, or the need for foundations, both in accelerating the demise of existing buildings and in increasing the cost of new ones. Others doubted whether these effects would be incurred with a rise of temperature of only $3°C$. Realistic pricing of energy would be needed, however, and this could have an effect on agriculture (eg through the fertilizer industry). It was suggested that wind and wave power could be used to reduce energy costs.

ACTION NEEDED TO AMELIORATE THE 'GREENHOUSE EFFECT'
This discussion dealt broadly with land use, the actions needed by the farming industry and the needs for research.

Land use policy and the agricultural industry

On land use and countryside implications, it was thought unwise to develop and build too widely on agricultural land because this would limit subsequent changes in use. There would be a need to have a means of managing change to ensure countryside and wildlife conservation. The suggestion that forestry may decline needed consideration in terms of a national reappraisal of land use. Agroforestry and energy forestry may both have attractions under the scenarios presented. It was pointed out that modern agriculture itself makes heavy use of energy and fossil fuels and that wider application of low-input systems is needed to reduce this.

A number of answers had therefore been given to the question posed in the opening of the general discussion, as to what can be done by farmers. They could directly reduce the greenhouse effect through changes in management. They could also help to identify critical points where research is needed.

RESEARCH NEEDS AND RESEARCH FUNDING

Throughout the discussion there were many suggestions for areas of research to help the industry respond to the huge challenges posed by the greenhouse effect. Global climatic models are central to prediction of the effects, and much work is needed to improve the precision of the predictions. Many of the feedback mechanisms in the system are not fully understood and more data are needed, for example on heat flux, circulation and biological activity in the oceans. Caution is necessary in predicting local effects since these are based on relatively few data.

Field studies

The theoretical effect of CO_2 enrichment on tree growth was discussed and the need for field trials with trees was stressed, including the effect on timber quality and on different species. The call for support of field trials was reinforced.

The question of field studies was raised again with the suggestion that much had already been done. Against this it was pointed out that this type of work had usually controlled only one of the many factors which might be involved in a new environment. Such experiments needed to be re-evaluated. For example, temperature gradients in crops, and increases in CO_2 throughout the life cycle of the crop would need to be studied so as to develop predictive, quantitative physiology modelling and responses in physiological plasticity. It would be very important that studies which have previously been done mostly in small-scale controlled environments, should be done on a field-scale, but with the ability also to vary moisture status, relative humidity and many other parameters that will change, but which have been little studied previously.

Funding

On research funding, the cuts being made in the UK at present were not considered to be having an adverse effect on the work on models of global climate since, for example, the Government gave an increase last year of 27% in the budget of the Natural Environment Research Council which is involved in that particular activity. The budget of the Agricultural and Food Research Council was viewed differently. Calculations on the volume of agricultural research in relation to the size of the industry had indicated a decline of some 50% in relative funding over the past 15 years. This could have serious long-term effects. Existing research capacity has to be used to undertake a new direction and meet new crises which may arise, and it takes time to develop experienced research workers.

One aspect of the reduced budgets is that it is currently very difficult to attract good candidates in sufficient number to fill studentships, and so meet the gaps in expertise which are caused by retirement. A reasonable balance needs to be achieved between attracting people into research and the level of commercial salaries.

There was no dissent to the view that the resources currently available are inadequate and that a vast increase is needed to answer the questions posed at the Conference. It had to be remembered, however, that the Government believes that 'near-market' research should be funded by those who would benefit directly from it. Thus, some of the cuts imposed by Government are cuts in public funding of research which the Government still believes should be carried out, but should be paid for by other sections of the community. Furthermore, some of the questions raised at the Conference about research were from groups of the agricultural industry which are large enough and rich enough to support the research which is needed.

Research needs

Research should be integrated, but not only in the UK or the EC. Global models need to be constructed by increased worldwide co-ordination. The immediate return on such research is very small and is not suitable for funding by the industry. There is a degree of urgency about this research which is not properly assessed by any government in the World at the present time, not withstanding the Montreal agreement on chloro-fluorocarbons. It was hoped that this meeting would impose a greater sense of urgency on our own Government for international collaboration on these matters.

A specific greenhouse effect is that nitrogen content in leaf, seed and grain is reduced when CO_2 levels are high. This has major implications for food quality, herbivore nutrition, insect relations and for pests and diseases, which need to be studied experimentally. It is important to ask about the sensitive points in crop and animal systems to determine what is a critical point of change in climate.

Grassland is a very complex community which is highly dependent on the interaction with the animal, and is a prime case where real experimental data are needed in order to model the effects. An overall view is needed – for example as to whether the effects in grassland would lead to overproduction or to extensive production. Much research is required and means of focussing on priorities are needed.

The Chairman referred to the Institute of Biology Natural Resources Policy Group which was studying the interface between agriculture and the environment. This Group would like to identify priorities in research, and participants were invited to provide lists, argued cases or papers to pass to the Institute of Biology Group.

CONCLUSIONS

The Chairman commented that some of the participants had found the technical level of the Conference beyond them at times. In his view, all were in that position for some parts of the topic. Few people could be highly competent technically across this enormous range of subjects. Nevertheless, the nature of the problem demands that discussions like this take place, and ways have to be found of communicating with others with different sorts of jargon. He concluded that this meeting was fairly successful in achieving that aim, and that in such a broad subject it would not be sensible to isolate the component parts for separate discussion. An overall view needs to be taken and the size of the topic is enormous.

Much research is clearly needed, particularly to reduce the uncertainties of prediction. Nevertheless, as the Prime Minister had concluded at the Downing Street seminar on the subject, which some of the participants of this Conference had attended, these uncertainties should not lead us to the conclusion that no action should be taken. Government-funded research over the next 5–10 years would allow better measures of these imponderables to be obtained. A vast amount of research is required and it is vital that this should be fully supported.

Bennett, R M (Ed) (1989) The 'greenhouse effect' and UK agriculture. CAS Paper 19. Reading: Centre for Agricultural Strategy.

Professor K J Treharne – a tribute

Professor Ken Treharne died suddenly in London a few hours after delivering his paper. The particularly lucid and forthright contribution which he made to the discussion on the cuts in agricultural research funding is printed here in full as a tribute to the great contribution which Ken Treharne made to the research which he so strongly defended.

Professor Treharne said "I believe the reductions in the research budgets that we've seen over recent years reflected to some extent a degree of a need to change. I think that Ken Blaxter analysed the position in respect of agricultural support of some 15 years ago, when indicating that if you took the whole of MAFF and AFRC, and those in universities involved in teaching or research in agricultural sciences, it represented something like one person per 14 farmers or per 1400 acres, which he said could well have been viewed as a fairly luxurious level of support. However, the rate of change of support that has occurred, notably in this decade, has taken that to more like 1 person per 30 farmers. He made the plea that enough is enough – that we are now in grave danger of missing opportunities, of eroding our science base to such an extent that we will not be in a position in the future to respond to desperate new needs and, notably, to provide the options for industry to maintain its competitive edge when one has a series of 'what if' questions such as we have been addressing today.

It has to be recognised that one of the largest problems that we have in coping with research cuts is that we are no longer in a position to develop our seed corn. We are trying to keep expertise alive. We are very successful in the way we are now persuading the private sector to work with us, and we have to recognise, quite correctly, that whilst we are losing funds in particular areas of work that my Council, AFRC, is involved with, there are genuine new funds coming in from Government which, like John (Dr John Bowman), I also applaud, and many of these are to underpin environmental issues. My own view is that, with the infrastructure we have, with the expertise of the science base of the UK with its world standing, we have gone far enough in these cuts and we need to re-evaluate what heritage my children and my grandchildren are going to have if the R & D base continues to suffer such massive erosion".

Appendix

List of authors

Dr J Bowman; Chief Executive of the National Rivers Authority, 30–34 Albert Embankment, London. (Formerly the Secretary of the Natural Environment Research Council).

Mr M Bradley; Ministry of Agriculture, Fisheries and Food, Stockbridge House Experimental Horticulture Station, Cawood, Selby, North Yorkshire.

Dr B A Callander; Head of Agricultural Meteorology, Meteorological Office, London Road, Bracknell, Berkshire.

Mr J Cochrane; Meteorological Office, London Road, Bracknell, Berkshire.

Dr J S Cox; Department of Physiology and Environmental Science, Nottingham University, School of Agriculture, Sutton Bonington, Loughborough, Leics.

Dr J Craigon; Department of Physiology and Environmental Science, Nottingham University, School of Agriculture, Sutton Bonington, Loughborough, Leics.

Dr B Denness; Bureau of Applied Sciences, Wydcombe Manor, Whitwell, Isle of Wight.

Dr R H Ellis; Plant Environment Laboratory, Department of Agriculture, University of Reading, Cutbush Lane, Shinfield, Reading, Berkshire.

Dr P Hadley; Department of Horticulture, School of Plant Sciences, University of Reading, Whiteknights, Reading, Berkshire.

The Rt Hon John MacGregor, OBE, MP; Minister of Agriculture, Fisheries and Food (up to 25th July 1989).

Professor J S Marsh; Head of the Department of Agricultural Economics and Management, Dean of the Faculty of Agriculture and Food, University of Reading, Earley Gate, Reading, Berkshire.

Mr R Matthews; Forestry Commission, Forest Research Station, Alice Holt Lodge, Wrecclesham, Farnham, Surrey.

Mr I F McKee; Department of Botany, University of Cambridge, Downing Street, Cambridge.

Dr R Mitchell; AFRC Institute of Arable Crops Research, Rothamsted Experimental Station, Harpenden, Hertfordshire.

Dr J I L Morison; Department of Meteorology, University of Reading, Earley Gate, Reading, Berkshire.

Professor M L Parry; Professor of Environmental Management, Atmospheric Impacts Research Group, School of Geography, University of Birmingham, Edgbaston, Birmingham.

Dr J R Porter; Department of Agricultural Sciences, University of Bristol, AFRC Institute of Arable Crops Research, Long Ashton Research Station, Bristol.

Dr P R Rowntree; Meteorological Office, London Road, Bracknell, Berkshire.

Professor E H Roberts; Professor of Crop Production, Plant Environment Laboratory, Department of Agriculture, University of Reading, Cutbush Lane, Shinfield, Reading, Berkshire.

Dr G R Squire; Department of Physiology and Environmental Science, Nottingham University, School of Agriculture, Sutton Bonington, Loughborough, Leics.

Dr D Stokes; Department of Agriculture and Horticulture, Nottingham University, School of Agriculture, Sutton Bonington, Loughborough, Leics.

Dr R J Summerfield; Plant Environment Laboratory, Department of Agriculture, University of Reading, Cutbush Lane, Shinfield, Reading, Berkshire.

Ms N Sweet; Department of Physiology and Environmental Science, Nottingham University, School of Agriculture, Sutton Bonington, Loughborough, Leics.

Professor K J Treharne; Director of Research, AFRC Institute of Arable Crops Research, Rothamsted Experimental Station, Harpenden, Hertfordshire.

Professor M H Unsworth; Department of Physiology and Environmental Science, Nottingham University, School of Agriculture, Sutton Bonington, Loughborough, Leics.

Professor P N Wilson; Professor of Agriculture and Rural Economy, The Edinburgh School of Agriculture, University of Edinburgh, West Mains Road, Edinburgh.

Professor H Woolhouse; Director of Research, AFRC Institute of Plant Science Research, John Innes Institute, Colney Lane, Norwich.

Centre for Agricultural Strategy

Sponsorship Scheme

The Centre gratefully acknowledges the long-term support under this scheme of the following firms:

Dow Elanco Ltd
ICI Agro Chemicals
Unilever plc

Centre Publications

Reports

1 *Land for Agriculture* (1976) £1.50.
2 *Phosphorus: a resource for UK agriculture* (1978) £1.75.
3 *Capital for agriculture* (1978) OUT OF PRINT.
4 *Strategy for the UK dairy industry* (1978) £2.95.
5 *National food policy in the UK* (1979) £2.85.
6 *Strategy for the UK forest industry* (1980) OUT OF PRINT.
7 *The efficiency of British agriculture* (1980) £2.85.
8 Jollans, J L (Ed) (1985) *The teaching of Agricultural Marketing in the UK* £6.00.
9 Jollans, J L (1985) *Fertilisers in UK farming* £8.00.
10 Craig, G M, Jollans, J L & Korbey, A (Eds) (1986) *The case for agriculture: an independent assessment* £9.50.
11 Carruthers, S P (Ed) (1986) *Alternative enterprises for agriculture in the UK* £9.50.
12 Carruthers, S P (Ed) (1986) *Land-use alternatives for UK agriculture* £3.00.
13 Harrison, A & Tranter, R B (1989) *The changing financial structure of farming* £8.95.

Papers

1 Marsh, J S (1977) *UK agricultural policy within the European Community* £1.50.
2 Tranter, R B (Ed) (1978) *The future of upland Britain* Proceedings of a symposium organised by CAS in conjunction with the Department of Agriculture and Horticulture, 19–22 September 1977 OUT OF PRINT.
3 Harrison, A, Tranter, R B & Gibbs, R S (1977) *Landownership by public and semi-public institutions in the UK* £1.75.
4 Collins, E J T (1978) *The economy of upland Britain, 1750–1950: an illustrated review* £2.20.
5 McCalla, A F (1978) *International agricultural research: potential impact on world food markets and on UK agricultural strategy* OUT OF PRINT.

6 Swinbank, A (1978) *The British interest and the green pound* £1.50.

7 Robbins, C J (Ed) (1978) *Food, health and farming: reports of panels on the implications for UK agriculture* £2.40.

8 Ritson, C (1980) *Self-sufficiency and food security* £2.00.

9 Tranter, R B (Ed) (1981) *Smallfarming and the Nation* Proceedings of a conference organised by the Smallfarmers' Association, 27 March 1980 £2.00.

10 Jollans, J L (Ed) (1981) *Grassland in the British economy* Proceedings of a symposium organised by the Department of Agriculture and Horticulture, the Department of Agricultural Economics and Management, the Grassland Research Institute and the Centre for Agricultural Strategy, 15–17 September 1980 £10.00.

11 Marshall, B J & Tranter, R B (Eds) (1982) *Smallfarming and the Rural Community* Proceedings of a conference organised by the Smallfarmers' Association, 26 March 1981 OUT OF PRINT.

12 Hallam, D (1983) *Livestock development planning: a quantitative framework* OUT OF PRINT.

13 Carruthers, S P & Jones, M R (1983) *Biofuel production strategies for UK agriculture* OUT OF PRINT.

14 Jollans, J L (1983) *Agriculture and human health* Report of a study and the proceedings of a symposium, 11–13 July 1983 £10.50.

15 Tranter, R B (Ed) (1983) *Strategies for family-worked farms in the UK* Proceedings of a symposium organised by the Smallfarmers' Association and the Centre for Agricultural Strategy, 21–22 September 1983 £7.50.

16 Korbey. A (Ed) (1984) *Investing in rural harmony: a critique* £5.00.

17 Korbey, A (Ed) (1985) *Food production and our rural environment – The way ahead* £5.50.

18 Miller, F A & Tranter, R B (Eds) (1988) *Public perception of the countryside* Proceedings of a conference organised by the Centre for Agricultural Strategy, 7 January 1988 £4.50.

19 Bennett, R M (Ed) (1989) *The 'greenhouse effect' and UK agriculture* Proceedings of a conference organised by the Centre for Agricultural Strategy, 14 July 1989.

Studies (in association with Knight Frank & Rutley)

1 Harvey, D R (1985) *Milk quotas; freedom or serfdom?* OUT OF PRINT.

2 Revell, B J (1985) *EC structures policy and UK agriculture* OUT OF PRINT.

3 Beard, N F (1986) *Against the grain? The EC cereals policy* OUT OF PRINT.

Joint Publications

1 *Agriculture: the triumph and the shame. An independent assessment* (1983) (published in collaboration with the Centre for European Agricultural Studies, Wye College, University of London) £5.00.

2 Choe, Z R (1986) *A strategy for pasture improvement by smallfarmers in upland Korea* (published in collaboration with Gyeonsang National University, Korea) £10.00.

3 Ansell, D J & Done, J T (1988) *Veterinary Research and Development: Cost benefit studies on products for the control of animal diseases.* Published jointly with the British Veterinary Association.

Occasional Papers

Harvey, D R, Barr, C J, Bell, M, Bunce, R G H, Edwards, D, Errington, A J, Jollans, J L, McClintock, J H, Thompson, A M M & Tranter, R B (1986) *Countryside implications for England and Wales of possible changes in the Common Agricultural Policy.* Main report, £20.00; Executive summary, £4.00.

Mailing list

To receive notification of future publications please ask to be put on the mailing list. To receive invoiced copies of future publications, please ask to be put on the standing order list.

Orders

All publications available from: The Centre for Agricultural Strategy, University of Reading, 1 Earley Gate, Reading RG6 2AT. Telephone: (0734) 318150. Prices quoted include postage. All Out of Print publications are available in facsimile.